The Call of the Flute, the Legend of Mirabai

Ondine Webb De Mer

COPYRIGHT

Acknowledgements and Permissions

Bhagavad Gita As It Is by Swami A.C. Bhaktivedanta Prabhupada published by Bhaktivedanta Book Trust 2001. Reprinted by permission of Robert Burnside /Bhaktivedanta Book Trust International, Inc. All rights reserved.

The Devotional Poems of Mirabai translated by A.J. Alston published by Motilal Banarsidass 1980. All rights reserved. Reprinted by permission of publisher.

The Devotional Poems of Mirabai translated by Shreeprakash Kurl published by Calcutta Writer's Workshop 1973. Reprinted by permission of publisher/Ananda Lal.

For Love of the Dark One: Songs of Mirabai translated by Andrew Schelling published by Shambala Press 1993. Reprinted by permission of Andrew Schelling and publisher/Dasya Zuccarello.

Manushi magazine 50-2, 1988 , *Women Bhakta Poets* edited by Madhu Kishwar and Ruth Vanita, published by Manushi Trust. By permission of Madhu Kishwar.

Mirabai: Ecstatic Poems translated by Robert Bly and Jane Hirshfield published by Beacon Press 2004. Reprinted by permission of Bly and Hirshfield and the publisher/Claire Desroches.

The Path of the Mystic Lover by Bhaskar Bhattacharyya with Nik Douglas and Penny Slinger published by Inner Traditions International and Bear & Company 1993. All rights reserved. Reprinted with permission of publisher/Maria Loftus.

Says Meera: An Anthology of Devotional Songs of Meera, India's Greatest Woman Poet translated by Vijay Munshi published by Nirala Publications 2001. By permission of Vijay Munshi.

Songs of the Saints of India by John Stratton Hawley and J.M. Jurgensmeyer published by Oxford University Press 1988. By permission of the publisher/Ben Kennedy.

Teachings of the Hindu Mystics by Andrew Harvey published by Shambala Press 2001. Reprinted by permission of Andrew Harvey and assistant Anne Andrews.

.

TABLE OF CONTENTS

Introduction

PART III, RECAPITULATION: Through the Blue Door

The Call of the Flute, The Legend of Mirabai

Listen to the melodious music of the Divine Poet.
He plays upon the Flute of Love-
The notes soar to heaven and reach the distant stars,
And dance on the raging waves of the sea.
The earth, the sea, the sky, the stars,
Are all woven together by the soft strains of the divine music.
Its vibrations echo through the corridors of time,
In the endless canopy of the sky.
Sama Veda 446

When you love you should not say
God is in my heart.
But rather, I am in the heart of God.
Kahlil Gibran, *The Prophet*

I am the words and you are the melody,
I am the melody and you are the words.
Traditional *mantra* after *Sapta-Padi*

Flower-like are the heels of the wanderer.
Thus his body grows and is fruitful.
All his sins disappear,
Slain by the toil of his journeying.
Aitareya Brahmana 7-15

Kanu bina gita nahi. (Without Krishna there is no song) Bengali
verse

INTRODUCTION

Part fantasy novel, part religious history, part personal memoir, *The Call of the Flute, The Legend of Mirabai* is essentially a work of fiction. Mirabai is an actual historical Hindu princess, poet, and devotee of Krishna born around 1498 into a royal family of Rajasthan. This novel of the imagination blends the few known recorded facts with legends to give an impression or experience of what her life might have been. There are many highly divergent translations of her poetry and some of these pieces called *padas* are of an autobiographical nature which round out what is known about her. The poetry quoted at the opening of some of the chapters is from Mirabai.

These incidents are widely accepted either historically or through legend: the *murti* given to Mira as a child by the *guru* Raidas, the play wedding presided over by her mother, the companionship of the *sakhi* Lalita, the arranged marriage to Bhoj Raj of Chittor, the persecution of Mira by her brother in law Vikram which included imprisonment in a tower, the cup of poison, the venomous snake, the bed of nails, and the order to drown herself. It is said that Akbar and Tansen came to Chittor in secret to hear Mira's music and gave her a costly necklace. She is also known to have traveled to Vrindavana where she encountered Jiva Goswami and an unknown *sadhu* who attempted seduction. Chaitanya is an actual historical figure who lived around the same time as Mira, but it is unknown if they ever met. And she did go to Dwarka with her life ending there under mysterious circumstances as I have written. The cutting of the braid and Mira's subsequent disappearance are still spoken of in India today.

I have imagined Mira's magical conception and birth, her Sacred Marriage to Krishna, the association of Bhoj Raj with Arjuna, the unknown *sadhu* as a Baul, the journey across the Thar, the meeting with Chaitanya, and the *Ban Yatra* pilgrimage. To enhance the story line, I have taken some liberties with the geographical layout of India and the traditional *Ban Yatra*.

The sections told by the narrator are all based on actual experiences and dreams I have had. Though I am a classical pianist, I always say I want to be a singer of art songs in my next life. The concept of music as the language of the spirit was first suggested to me by my Piano Professor Dr. Patricia LaLiberte during my undergraduate studies with her at the University of Minnesota Duluth, 1976-8. The epitaph I have used for my piano studio since 1980 is from Kahlil Gibran: "Music is the language of the spirit. It opens the door to the secrets of life, bringing peace, abolishing strife."

The narrator's assessment by her mentor at the beginning of *Hanged Man* is one I received from Dr. Carl (Chuck) Lofy who taught classes on Jung and Joseph Campbell at Mankato State University in Minnesota. In 1980 shortly after I had finished my Master's in Piano Performance, I began my first teaching position and he came to me for lessons. At the time I was baffled by his remarks; now after many life experiences I understand more of his meaning and am still seeking to this day for all I can be.

The sections about the Chai House and the Temple of the Peacock come directly from my encounter at The Wayhouse of Light in Madison, Wisconsin, courtesy of "outsider artist" Mona Boulware Webb, Christmas Day 1980. The decor with the beaded curtains, the spiral staircase, the vibrant murals, the artifacts from many cultures in a cave-like shrine room, and the massive standing candelabra that was lit for me are all authentic. The magical ambience of Mamounia, a now closed Moroccan restaurant on Capitol Hill in Seattle, influenced the decor of the tea room in Chai House.

Many of the dreams of the Eternal Beloved have been mine and I have had a recurring nightmare for many years that is similar to the one I describe. The chanting experience took place at the Siddha Yoga Meditation Temple in Seattle sometime around 2004 and it was in this setting that Surabhi the Sacred Cow came to me and I imagined the journey through Her Divine Eye to Vrindavana. From this event the idea of the novel was initially born, although I had been reading Mira's poetry for some time.

I try to express my experience of being a mother to my son Paul in the writing about the blue-skinned child, especially how I felt when I looked into his eyes for the first time. I am indebted to the book *Feeding Your Demons* by Tsultrim Allione as an antidote to stage fright; the experience with the Guardian of the Portal comes directly from the work I did there. I envisioned the *Rasa Lila* to be similar to a Full Moon Dance and Worship Circle I attended in a forest grove one summer in Minneapolis with Antiga as High Priestess in the late 1980s. The *Ban Yatra* descriptions were benefitted by my childhood trips to an outdoor park in a wooded setting called Fairyland in Bovey, Minnesota and also my love of *The Wizard of Oz* movie. And finally, in *Maya the Veil of Illusion, Recapitulation*, and *Coda*, I convey experiences I had in the 60s as a flower child during my brief experiments with mescaline and other mind altering drugs. At the time, I absolutely knew the secrets of the universe, but found I could not express them in words afterwards.

In my work and my life, I have been deeply influenced by Kahil Gibran's *The Prophet* and Joseph Campbell's mono myth of the hero's journey. The character of Aslan in *The Chronicles* of *Narnia* by

C.S. Lewis, and his effect on his followers, has shaped my feelings about the blue child, who is also God in unusual form. From the writings of Lewis, the concept of *sehnsucht* , that ardent and unrequited longing in the human heart to unearth and embrace the ever elusive mystery of life and become one with the Divine, has always been a driving force for me long before I knew the name for it. This yearning, expressed through the achingly beautiful Call of the Flute from afar, is the essential component in Mira's experience of Krishna and in the narrator's dreams of the Eternal Beloved.

The writing of this novel has been a joy and never felt like work to me. For over fifteen years, despite putting the manuscript away for long periods of time to incubate, it has given my life a tremendous spark of creativity and allowed me to express my deepest inner landscape. Born under the sign of Sagittarius, I love research and study as well as journeying. My mode of travel is inner and it has taken me to fantastical realms. I am indebted to all those who provided me with the experiences that shaped the narrator's section of the book, for these were priceless gifts that can never be duplicated and have made me who I am today.

PART I: Exposition: The Call of the Flute

1. Prelude: Invocation

Whenever and wherever there is a decline in religious practice,

and a predominant rise in irreligion-

at that time I descend Myself.

4.7 (Prabhupada 136)

Lord Krishna, *Bhagavad Gita*

Long ago in The Time before Time, magic and myth were alive in the hearts and minds of the people of ancient India. The Gods and Goddesses roamed the earth. It is said in the *Puranas*, the most ancient scriptures of India, that God, the Supreme One, will incarnate on this earth in times of dire need to save the world and our way of life from utter destruction. This Descent of the Divine comes to participate in the life of humanity, bringing the return of *shanti*, the ultimate peace that passes understanding, to the souls of all beings.

And so it has been that Vishnu, the Loving Protector, Lord of Law and Order in the Universe, has descended to earth nine times to come to humankind's aid. He has been the Fish Matsya, the Tor-

6

toise Kurma, the Boar Varaha, the Man-Lion Narisimha, the Dwarf Vamana, Rama of the Ax called Parasurama, the young king Rama, Krishna the Blue God, and the Buddha. Shining like a comet in the sky, He will appear for the final time as Kalki the White Horse, so this earth may become the *paradise* it is meant to be. It is with Vishnu's eighth incarnation as the Lord Krishna, the *Purna Avatara* or Complete One, that this tale is concerned.

In a dark time of much wickedness and injustice in the land, Mother Earth assumed the form of Surabhi the Sacred Cow and visited the gods in their mountain abode to plead for the healing of Her body, the Earth. The God Vishnu, in His role as Guardian of the Cosmos, decreed He would return once again to earth, for the eighth time, reborn in the form of a wondrous blue skinned child of joy and delight. This child Krishna, accompanied by His Companion the Sacred Cow, would bring blessings to all devotees. The Lord Vishnu has chosen Vrindavana as His abode or holy *dhama*. He will come to share in the joys and sorrows of the people, living as a man among men. He will come to reveal to this world the magnificent beauty of God.

Oh come, Krishna, Shyam the Dark One who is the blue color of the Infinite Sky, Manamohan the Enchanter of Hearts, Giridhara the Lifter of Mountains, Hari the Abductor Who robs His Devotees of

7

all their sins, Gopala the Sacred Cowherd, Madan the Intoxicator. Give us the vision of your Divine Eye and open our perceptions to the pure love of devotion so we may experience your sacred and enchanting presence. Be with us in this tale so we may see into the heart of our heroine Mirabai, Rajput princess, archetypal *bhakta,* Lover of God, who carried You within her soul and sang Your praises in her *padas* and in her way of life. Let us all become *bhaktas,* the Beggars of God, in our search for enlightenment.

2. <u>The Dream</u>

I do not know how to meet my Lord.

He came into my courtyard and went.

And I only know that I missed Him.

I spend days in search,

Scanning the road night and day.

Hari came into my courtyard,

But, wretch that I am, I was asleep.

The pain of absence burns my bewildered heart

And gives me no rest.

(#43 Alston 52)

For many months now I have been dreaming each night, dreams of my search for the Eternal Beloved. Seeking and searching, always I hear in the background the Call of a Flute drawing me near. I have found the Desire of my Heart over and over again, and the longing I feel is all consuming, full of hope and the potential for great joy. I would give all that I am, all that I have, to be in the presence of the Beloved for even one moment.

Each time I dream, the plot is slightly different like a Theme and Variations; the face, gender, and form of the Beloved varies. Sometimes the Beloved comes in human form as a blue skinned laughing child, an ancient *guru*, a compassionate mother or protec-

9

tive father, a confidante or close companion, a golden being who shows the path, a divine musician, a community of like-minded seekers, a twin born from the same womb, or my soul mate and lover. Other times my Heart's Desire appears as an animal- a white cow with warm brown eyes, or a peacock whose myriad feathers contain eyes that are gazing at me. In all of these images, the eyes, whether human or animal, look into my innermost soul and see who I truly am, what I can truly be, encouraging me to reach for my highest potential.

My Heart's Desire can appear as a part of nature- a sacred river, an exotic garden, an orchard of purple plum trees, a forest of Banyan trees that seem to be   growing upside down. Sometimes the Beloved is a place- a golden city by the sea, a green and fertile oasis, a sacred grove deep within the forest, an island with murmuring water on all sides, a place where I will find ultimate and eternal peace, a place I long to be with all of my heart. Then I feel a tremendous sense of nostalgic yearning for a home I have only dreamt of and never known, a deep desire to return to the Land of my Soul, to Paradise, to the Garden of Eden.

Often there is something magical, spiritual, and exotic about the imagery, something I connect to a legendary land far away in time and place. In the background of the dream I hear the haunting call of a flute in harmony with the poetic chanting of a woman who sings with a stunning voice in a language I do not know. My heart's desire may even take the ephemeral form of this beautiful melody I long to make mine. Often I see a profusion of these images in rapid succession. Everything is mixed up and yet connected, shifting and turning like the patterns in a kaleidoscope, always creating something diverse and fascinating, never returning to the same combination of shapes, colors, and forms.

But like a tragic novel of thwarted destiny, each time, in every dream, I merely brush auras with the Beloved, barely touching, just enough to know the possibility of what could be. Night after night, in endless permutation, I experience this near connection and unutterable loss, and always, the dream brings the same set of wrenching emotions. Somehow, something conspires every time to make us nearly connect; it is oh so close, but not quite close enough. We miss the connection and the linking up of our energies by centimeters, often mere moments or split seconds in time, and are sent in opposite directions, wheeling off into the cosmos of *karma* and reincarnation.

Often a blue mist materializes in the dream, obscuring the scene and creating an almost invisible but impenetrable barrier. This mist is so ethereal in appearance it could be the work of *Maya*, the Goddess of Illusion. And yet I cannot pass though it or even see what lies beyond. I am unable to part this Veil between the Worlds and the treasures that lie out of reach can only be imagined.

Sometimes as I am approaching, the Beloved moves further and further away from me and I can never reach out to touch my heart's desire. Then this fleeting image fades from my sight, getting small-er and more distant, wavering like a mirage. Eventually the vision vanishes into nothingness as if it had never been there. I feel as though I am stretching beyond my mortal limits, my bones and sinews straining to grasp and hold on to a mere hallucination of my heart's desire.

In another dream, a kindly old Ferrier arrives in a boat. But I must wade out into the water and I cannot seem to reach him though he is smiling and beckoning to me. And so the Ferrier moves on to transport some other more able seeker. Another time an ancient crone stands before me looking at me with compassion but shak-ing her head saying "No, it is not yet your time." She shows me a strange image of a man hanging upside down from a tree, but I cannot understand what it means.

Although most dreams are benign despite the intensity of the long-ing and lack of attainment, some can be more frightening like a warning. There may be a Guardian who protects the Beloved and I am judged unworthy. In one dream, a fiercely angry man in a turban violently pushes me away, warding me off with flaming swords. Other times the great walls of a fortress are being erected around me right before my eyes, holding me in a tall, narrow tower like a prison separating me from the Beloved and isolating me from all human contact. My body is paralyzed as I stand in place allowing my enclosure. I am contained in a barren, sterile room and can see nothing beyond the walls. In my prison I am offered only a cup of water, but I know it is poison and so I cannot drink. I am more completely and utterly alone than I have ever been in my entire life. And I am literally dying of thirst, gasping for a drink from the pure, sweet Waters of Life that is never offered to me.

In another version of the dream there is some kind of a dance within a circle. Everything is a blur of motion and energy. I hear sublime celestial music, chanting, chiming, and singing. Accompanied by the flute, the voice of a woman weaves in and out of the blend but I cannot see who the singer is. This miraculously beautiful voice sounds much like mine but enhanced with a power and depth of expression I do not possess and would give my very soul to attain. I want so much to join in this celebration of life. But there is some invisible barrier that repulses me and keeps me out. No one seems to notice my presence and I am only an unidentified, unnamed spectator. Occasionally I can see many hands reaching out to me but I am unable to grasp them and they withdraw with empty, sad arms beyond my reach.

Each time, I am left with a heart rending sense of separation and longing for what could have been, stuck in the returning cycle of *samsara*, our worldly existence of birth, life, death, and rebirth. My heart is breaking in anguish and yet there is always a glimmer of hope for what might be possible. I know I will do what I must to attain the fruits of this yearning, even giving up my entire life as I know it, for union with the Eternal Beloved is the very essence of what makes life worth living. But despite the pain of this unfulfilled longing and the implicit warning in some of the dreams, I continue on in my life without question, making no adjustments.

3. <u>Nightmare</u>

Without Shyam I cannot survive.

Charmed by thy beauty, O my Beloved

I offer Thee my body, life, and mind.

I have lost all appetite for food and drink

And my eyes have gone dim.

O Murari, day and night

I dream of meeting Thee,

When shall I have Thy sight?

Days and nights pass

As I call upon Thee.

O Hari, without Thee

my life flickers feebly on.

(#69 Alston 62)

Lately my dream has turned more nightmarish and I am left shaken after each recurrence. Often I awaken screaming, sweating, and disoriented. I am alone, lost in an endless desert of sand. It is like trudging through a Wasteland in search of a Holy Grail that doesn't even exist. I can no longer see the face of my Beloved or make even the slightest connection to my Heart's Desire. Paralyzed with a heavy inertia, I cannot move forward, though I know I am desperately trying to reach something or someone. I have even forgotten what it is I seek.

In the dream, it is the darkest time of night. The howling winds of a barren desert sound like wailing banshees, the portents of death. A relentless, primal energy begins to sting my skin, dulls my mind, and covers my body until I am buried in a tomb of sand. Like salt, the grains of sand burn and irritate every pore of my body. The thirst of the desert is endless and without limits. It can never be satisfied or quenched. This unfulfilled need sucks dry everything in its path like a greedy vulture, annihilating all life. I am sinking down, descending into despair. The spark of my hope, the very light of my life, is being extinguished by the fury of a terrifying desert windstorm that leaves nothing alive in its path. This suffocating sensation brings a loss of identity that is all consuming; I am nothing and no one, even my voice is completely gone. There is no possibility of escape, no place to hide or find shelter, and yet, I still ferociously fight the knowledge of my demise in the face of such utter hopelessness. I want life at any cost.

I try to awaken myself to stop the inevitable progression of my nightmare, but I can only lie helplessly immobilized as though drugged until I have disintegrated into nothingness each time. I feel myself drying up, losing the precious moisture of life and soon I become mere dust, mingled with the sands of the desert, the essence of my soul lost forever in the timeless landscape. It is as though I have never existed. I have died and there is nothing more, no rebirth, no enlightenment, no ascension into a heavenly paradise, only darkness and nothingness.

During the days that follow each occurrence of this nightmare, I am exhausted and find it difficult to focus, my thoughts scattered like the grains of sand in the desert dreamscape. I am haunted by the intense and frightening imagery and feel myself becoming more and more high-strung and edgy. At night when I want to rest, insomnia plagues me in fear of becoming entrapped in the nightmare again. The dream is beginning to take its toll on my mind and when I sing in my practice sessions, I can imagine my voice cracking under the heat of the desert sun. Though I am beginning to feel some fear and stage fright before my concerts, I am grateful thus far to be able to lose myself in the music. But I am starting to feel underneath it all, that something deeply essential to my very soul may be missing in my life.

I cannot say for certain why the dreams began, but they come after an extraordinary occurrence. At this particular evening's concert, I am blessed with a peak experience, one of only a handful I have had in my entire life. Although my singing is always accomplished and at a high professional level, this time I have gone far beyond myself. I am no longer the Singer, I am the Song. The music comes through me as if directly from the Master Composer/Creator

Himself. I become a channel like a high priestess or a goddess with a gift that I give unstintingly and effortlessly. And I am literally floating on air. It feels as though God is in the audience and I am making a sacred offering.

Following the concert, I am in my dressing room receiving congratulations from my audience. An unusual family group approaches to greet and thank me. The lilt of their melodious speech has an exotic intonation and the woman wears a *saari*. The husband is much older, more like a guardian to the serene woman. With them is a handsome dark young boy. He is so dark his skin is almost blue in hue and he is wearing some unusual earrings I have never seen before.

I am so drawn to the boy's charming manner and dazzling smile that I cannot look more closely at the earrings. My eyes are blinded by tunnel vision, for I can see nothing but his enchanting face. For me, there is no one else in the room, only the blue boy and I, as if we two were alone in a universe all of our own. I am completely flooded by the joyous feeling of connection we share, dazzled by the ecstasy of this moment. The child is absolutely exuberant in his enjoyment of my music, telling me I sing as beautifully as their beloved Saint Mirabai. The family moves on to allow my other admirers to speak with me and I wish I could hold on to him forever.

But after everyone has departed and I am alone there is a knock on my door. It is the child again. He has a gift for me in appreciation of the music. Suddenly he is shy, quickly gives me his offering, and darts away. On second look, I have the impression that the earrings he wears are in the shape of a crocodile, but he moves so quickly I cannot distinguish them for certain. Within the wrappings enclosing his gift is an exotic statue, a worn, much loved antique *murti*, a miniature figurine of a flute player with blue skin. I recognize Him as Krishna, the God of Music and Love. I place Him on my altar at home and soon the dreams begin.

4. <u>Chai House</u>

Despite my successful and rapidly growing career, my teacher/ mentor has told me there is much more I am meant to do with my life. I am taken aback and annoyed by his perplexing comments, for I have worked very hard to achieve my goals and sacrificed a large portion of my existence outside of music to be at this level. I have sought and found the Beloved of my Heart in music, or so I think. My entire identity has been fashioned around my work, and yet my mentor is telling me I am capable of doing something else, something more. And it is clear he does not mean musically. It has something to do with my destiny or spirit, but he does not elaborate and I will not ask. I don't want to hear it; this is my chosen life. But when I consider my repeated dreams, some subconscious thought nags at the back of my brain agreeing with his assessment, questioning and considering his words, wondering if I am missing something.

On my altar, the *murti* stands inanimate and mute. But its image has shown up in my dreams for several nights in a row. The dream comes in the form of an animated cartoon. The *murti* of Krishna comes to life with a beguiling smile and begins to laugh with uproarious delight. The Blue God looks directly into my eyes and starts to talk to me. But I can't understand one word. It is all a jumbled gibberish of nonsensical syllables to my ears. I am certain He is speaking in English but it sounds to me like some alien language from outer space. Krishna shrugs His shoulders, winks at me, and begins to play His flute, haunting my soul with the wordless language of His music as if to say "this is what I mean." He no longer tries to engage me and seems to be unaware of my presence, for He is lost in the timeless melody of the flute. I too am lost as if spellbound and awaken in a floating ecstasy.

Tonight I have gone to a quaint little Chai House in an unfamiliar part of town, for I have been told that there is a gypsy crone who reads the tarot in a back room of the shop. Having shared my recurrent dreams and troubling nightmare with friends, it has been suggested that I may find an answer here in this place. And the words of my mentor haunt me, bringing out a curious feeling of wonderment and yearning I cannot explain. With a sense of adventure and a little apprehension, I decide to consult the Reader.

The Chai House is in a neighborhood in the oldest part of town, comprised of tiny, unique shops reminiscent of a bazaar. The place has no name, only a simple sign that says Chai House to mark the location. The main floor is submerged below street level by a set of stairs. Ornate *jaali* screens enclose and shelter the windows. I try to peer into the unlit darkness within, but cannot see clearly because of the patterned latticework. The door is locked. Then I notice another door to the side, which leads up a steep set of stairs to a veranda or balcony full of arched windows. There are little domes on the roof making it look like an exotic Indian *mandir* or a miniature Taj Mahal. Colorful lanterns decorate the balcony glowing softly in the evening light.

I climb the stairs and find the door is unlocked despite the late hour. Inside are small low tables with embroidered and mirrored pillows on the floor for seating. The carved *jaali* screens filter in the lights of the evening, creating scintillating patterns on the floor. Tapestries and sheer fabrics adorn the walls making it appear to be the tent of a maharajah or a sheik of the desert. I am greeted by an attendant who seats me at one of the tables and asks me to wash my hands in warm scented water. It feels to me like an act of purification before a solemn and sacred ritual. The shop is strangely empty of other customers but I am welcomed in as if expected. She asks me what I seek.

When I say that I am here for a reading, I am taken by the hand and led forward. Hidden behind a large decorative screen in the Chai House is a spiral staircase that is hung with beaded curtains like a waterfall of sparkling gemstones. As if in a fantasy scene from an enchanted fairy tale, I descend down the stairs to the lower floor. At the bottom, the entrance is shielded by the jeweled curtains, which are parted for me by the attendant.

5. <u>Hanged Man</u>

To my surprise, I enter a secret room that feels subterranean and cave-like after being upstairs in the aerie. It is adorned like a miniature temple with oriental carpets and exotic hangings over the windows. On every wall, fabulous psychedelic murals have been painted in vibrant colors. The imagery is a combination of the elements of nature with trees, birds, and flowers which gleam like precious gemstones. Amidst the exotic and lush flora of the scenery, beautiful faces peep through, all with large glowing eyes. In each of the many niches within the room is a deity from a different culture and mythology of the world. And there at a low table that has been made into an altar sits the gypsy reader acting as High Priestess.

I am immediately at ease in her presence, for there is something reassuring about the maternal qualities of the Old One. She says I may call her Amma or Grandmother. Around her neck she wears an amulet of a dark skinned youth playing the flute. I think I should recognize the charm, for it seems similar somehow to the *murti* gifted to me by the young boy after my concert. But I cannot consciously make the connection. Even so, I am already stepping outside of the comfortable, carefully constructed realm of my life on the stage in music.

She asks me what I seek and listens impassively without comment or question as I describe the dreams. Candles and incense are lit. Holding hands, we sit together in peace for a moment and then she tells me to shuffle the cards and lay them face down.

The backs are mesmerizing, filled with tiny silver stars, moons, suns, and other mystic symbols on a pale blue background. They twinkle gently in the pale candle light and draw me in. I am to choose the one that calls to me when I feel ready. As the Old One turns over my chosen card I see a strange and unfamiliar image. She calls it the Hanged Man. He is hanging upside down from one of his legs on a flowering tree that looks like a cross. His face and head are glowing and his expression conveys a feeling of peace and acceptance, even of joy. His pose reminds me of a graceful yoga *asana* or posture and he appears to be an organic part of the tree. I sense that somewhere I might have seen this image before, perhaps in my dreams.

Literally staring into the deepest part of my soul where I cannot hide, she asks me again, quizzically, what I seek. I begin to cry. For suddenly I feel that endless and unfulfilled yearning of my dreams and the aching desire to reach and embrace my deepest longings for something mystical and magical that is beyond me, so far away. Yes, she says, "An essential part of your spirit has not yet come forth to claim you, and that is what you seek. We can call this your Eternal Beloved, your Heart's Desire, the Circle of Endless Love, the Holy Grail, or many other names for the Divine."

The Gypsy says the image on the card is the Cosmic Tree of Life called *Asvattha*. This tree is the mythical upside-down tree that connects one to the divine. It is a wish fulfilling tree and here a Seeker may ask for her heart's desire. She says that the card indicates a test and a sacrifice in the future. I must experience a complete reversal of my way of life in order to transform the dream into a vision of harmony and wholeness. I will undergo the death of all that I know and a resurrection into a new way of being, a rite of passage that is beyond my comprehension at this time. I must look at the world from upside down through the eyes of love, surrendering all my masks and protections. And I must agree to these conditions and face the unknown totally and completely alone. Only then will the dream change and the nightmare vanish. The Gypsy tells me I must understand that nothing will ever be the same again once I embark upon this path. She asks me if I will accept my *kismet* or destiny.

As I answer "yes," she looks deeply into my eyes and the excited and bewildered thoughts in my mind are stilled as she sees once again with her psychic vision my soul's destiny within me. She says that because I have a pure heart I am to go to the Temple of the Peacock and pick the plums from the grove there as an offering to Him. She says I must taste each plum first to be sure of the sweetness of my gift. They must be dark blue in color with skin like velvet, the color of His skin. "Whose skin," I ask, but she is already dismissing me and does not answer or even seem to hear my question.

When I ask how I will find this temple, she merely smiles and tells me to go by the Way of the Secret Path through the Tall Grass. With a distant look in her eyes, she seems to be no longer present in this time and place. She begins talking in riddles and rhymes like some ancient oracle: "Follow the Secret Path, see without sight, hear without sound, feel without touch. Go to the place where everything is music and song and listen with your soul to the melody that was composed for your ears alone." And she tells me to let the Call of the Flute guide me. She asks me for the second time if I will accept this challenge, asking now if I will embrace my destiny with all of my body, mind, soul, and heart. I have no doubts as I answer yes.

The Old One tells me I must be willing to let go of my ordinary vision to see through the Divine Eye, the *prema-netra* or Eye of Pure Love. She says my eyes will be anointed and I must hang from the Cosmic Tree of Life. She says that when I reach the Heart of Enlightenment, I will see the fruit of the *Asvattha* tree ripen and turn color, a deep, dark purple blue like the plums, like the color of His skin. Then I will know the One to Whom the fruit belongs, the One to Whom I belong. Only then will I come to my true Home. And she asks me for the third time, if I will embrace this Path, giving all that I am through the Heart of Love. The number three is the ancient charm to set the spell and again I answer yes making my choice a sacred and binding vow before the eyes of God.

The Gypsy Crone tells me I cannot return the way I came, by way of the spiral staircase, for "the leaf doesn't go back to the branch and life goes always forward." Pushing me swiftly towards the front door she says, "Go, time is of the essence." This is the night of the Sacred Dance and I must be ready. Only at this time, from this place, can I go to the realm where my quest will be answered. And the answers are for me alone, for no one else in the entire universe can find and enter this portal made only for me. This is the Cross-roads where all the possible choices and paths towards my destiny, like spokes on the Wheel of Life, intersect at the center of the circle, the place where I am meant to be. She enjoins me to remember the purple plums, for one must always bring a gift in return for the blessings of the Divine One.

To my surprise, the door that had been locked from the outside only a short time ago is now easily opened. As I begin to leave her, the Gypsy calls me back once more and says that she has a gift for me. She says that she is the Keeper of the Amulet and that now it is being passed to me. Quickly she removes the charm of the dark-skinned flute player from around her neck and places it over my head to rest upon my breast, at the center of my heart. She says it is a talisman for entry and return and that it must always remain close to remind me to have courage and faith, for all will be well no matter how it may seem. And she tells me "when you go through the Blue Door, the One that has No Key, you will be Home."

6. <u>The Secret Path Through the Tall Grass</u>

O Krishna, Charmer of Hearts,

Lifter of Mountains,

I hear your flute calling me-

Shall I come by the secret path through the tall grass?

O Lord of Heavenly Blue,

My heart cannot rest until we are together,

Until we walk along the banks of the Jamuna

deep into the night.

(Harvey 80-1)

Because the Gypsy has given me only vague directions, at first I begin walking aimlessly. The way I seek is well hidden and the streets twist and turn around and about until I have lost all rational sense of direction. There are many places where the path diverges and choices must be made. The streets are unnaturally hushed and deserted and there is no one to ask directions. I feel as though I am the only person in the entire city, perhaps in the whole universe.

But eventually it is almost as though an invisible path has been marked for me. I am drawn and guided by a mysterious, sweet melody that seems to come from a flute. It meanders in a sinuous spiral reminding me of a snake charmer's tune, breathy and restless. Humming in my mind, the sound becomes more intense as I walk on, the tempo quickening the pace of my steps. Despite my initial uncertainty, I no longer seem to have any question about which way to turn and my sense of intuition gets stronger as I approach the destination. I am certainly no longer on the familiar, well-trod and carefully defined path of my life in music.

Several times I have walked past and then turned back again sensing my journey's end nearby. But then I actually begin to hear the very faint strains of a yearning melody played by some unknown flute player and realize I have found what I seek. It is the same melody I heard humming in my mind as I walked, but tamed now into a slower processional marking my arrival at an important destination. I am being led to the place where everything is music and song, following the Secret Path through the Tall Grass that leads to nowhere in this world.

The temple grounds seem to be camouflaged in a blue mist keeping away those who do not have the eyes to see. It is only the song of the flute that confirms the spot. In the darkness of the evening, the place looks mysterious, but inviting. And yet, there is nothing memorable about what I see. The site is completely enclosed and surrounded by a thick grove of ancient trees which blocks the inside view. I push my way through a tiny opening in the dense foliage. Once inside, civilization is left behind; I am in another world.

Before me is an enclosure with an astonishing gated archway that leads towards a temple building. It is the entire tail of a peacock's plumage, displayed in openness and majesty, made up of two life-sized peacocks, one on each side of the gateway, with raised and open tails that blend together to create a canopy over the entrance. The feathers are richly colored in vibrant shades of sea mist aqua, midnight blue, and the green of emeralds and springtime. Surrounding the eyes are golden circles like the radiant sun, creating an aura of royalty and warmth. I think I must be dreaming, for the birds seem to be living, breathing creatures, shimmering with energy. Like surreal shape-shifters, at one moment they appear to be alive and gazing into my very soul, ready to question my intent or offer me a message. The next moment they are only superb pieces of artistry and illusion.

The opalescent glow of the peacock feathers has an eerie effect with hundreds of eyes that appear to be watching me intently. I feel as though the Divine Eyes of all the Gods and Goddesses that have ever been are observing every aspect of my being and my innermost soul in silent witness. I am utterly naked before them. In myth, I have read that the All-Seeing Eye knows past, present, and future and guards the Gates of Paradise. I am about to enter this sacred portal, heralded by the peacocks. As if by magic, the gate opens for me and I walk down the narrow path to the temple.

Beyond this gated entrance, the door to the temple is a simple, unmarked wooden structure, not the Blue Door the Gypsy spoke of. It is locked and the building is dark and silent. I try the door several times, attempting to force it open, and knock to no avail, the peacocks gazing at me impassively, waiting to see how I will respond, whether I will persevere in my quest. I am deeply puzzled and walk around the building several times looking for another entrance. But there is none. My uncertainty returns until I notice a hidden, wooded path to the side of the structure. The way is so well concealed, that no one would ever detect it unless they knew what to look for. This is surely the Secret Path the Gypsy spoke of, for the grass is tall and unkempt as though the place has been deserted for years and no one has walked this way in recent times.

The wooded path leads to a secluded walled garden with another gated entranceway. To my amazement I notice trees that are heavily fruited with the dark blue plums I am looking for, and so I gratefully pick some to take with me. The Call of the Flute is becoming stronger, more insistent, magnetizing my steps as I walk forward. Communicating excitement and impatience, the melody and rhythm are becoming more demanding and drive me forward. The flute calls compellingly to me and I am spellbound by these sinuous and exotic notes of pure magic.

7. <u>The Blue Boy, Child of My Heart</u>

At the portal to this Garden of Paradise there is a cluster of Indian cowbells, which I ring. Soon I hear excited child-like laughter and the patter of running feet. The door is opened for me with a push of high energy and I can see a miniature domed shrine further ahead. Before me in the doorway stands a beautiful young boy, so dark and dusky he is almost blue. I notice he is wearing earrings in the shape of a crocodile. He is so utterly adorable with his dimpled cheeks, dark curls, lustrous eyes, and soft, round flesh that I want to embrace him as if he were my own little son. His radiant smile lights up the entire universe. I feel a wondrous sense of simple, innocent happiness I have not known in a long time.

Though small in stature, his presence fills the portal, giving the impression that he is a miniature god merging his blue aura with the entryway. He seems so familiar to me, and yet I cannot imagine how I know him. The child is absolutely delighted to see me there, as though he has been waiting patiently for me and at long last I have arrived. Despite his welcoming overtures, I know that my acceptance into the inner sanctum is in his hands alone.

This precocious and charming child greets me with the greatest joy, clapping his hands with enthusiasm and jumping up and down as if dancing in ecstasy to see me. Before I can introduce myself and tell him how I have come to be there he begins to question me in earnest. He speaks in a lilting, melodious voice, addressing me by name with deep affection, putting me completely at ease with his ingratiating ways. Already, without my saying a word, he knows who I am and why I am here, but he wants to look into my soul in a deeper way. He has noticed with curiosity the amulet I am wearing and wants to know how I came by it. When I tell him that a Gypsy Crone placed it around my neck, he smiles knowingly without a hint of surprise. "Oh, that's Amma" he says.

He asks me what I seek and without hesitation I tell him it is my Eternal Beloved, my Heart's Desire. Without guile, he inquires whether I have brought him a gift and I remember the plums. Re-calling the words of the Gypsy, I taste several before finding the juiciest and sweetest offering. The Blue Child laughs in delight and takes the half eaten plum with a joyful and simple pleasure. Play-fully, we share several bites of the succulent fruit. We are feeding each other with the fruits of love like two children who have known each other forever and always been the best of friends.

Both the childlike and the maternal in me reach out to his beautiful nature and I am experiencing a kind of selfless, unconditional, and universal love I have never known before and only imagined in my dreams. There is an inexplicable feeling of exultation being in his presence, comparable only to falling in love at first sight. If I were a child, he would be my favorite playmate and best friend. If I were a mother, he would surely be my most beloved son. And yet, at the same time, there is something of the old soul in his eyes. Certainly, he is much, much more than what he appears to be. My love for him has already consumed my heart and soul, becoming an essential part of my being. His captivating presence beside me, and the sound of his melodious voice, makes and completes my entire world. Nothing else in the whole universe matters to me anymore except being here now with the blue boy. I have entered the Garden of Paradise and looked upon the Face of the Beloved.

Turning more serious, he imprints my forehead with the juice of a plum, making a *tilaka*, the auspicious mark of life, and bids me enter into the shrine with him. He tells me to close my eyes and open my heart to see and hear the world of nature as it truly is, allowing all sensory impression to come through my third eye. This all sounds so familiar, like an echo or variation of the singsong chant of the gypsy: "see without sight, hear without sound, feel without touch."

As I close my eyes, the blue skinned boy gently anoints them with a fragrance so sweetly intoxicating that it takes my breath away and makes my mind and body feel dream-like and totally relaxed. He has activated my *prema-netra*, the Eye of Pure Devotion and Love that will allow me to see the mystical worlds lying beyond the realm of mundane life. Acting entirely on trust and faith, I do as he asks and take his hand, allowing him to guide me.

8. *Maya*, the Veil of Illusion

The Song of the Flute, O sister, is madness.

I thought that nothing that was not God could hold me

But hearing that sound I lose mind and body,

My heart wholly caught in the net.

O flute, what were your vows, what is your practice?

What power sits by your side?

Even Mira's Lord is trapped in your seven notes.

(Bly/Hirshfield 13) Trans Hirshfield

My movement forward suddenly comes to an abrupt halt. I am stopped by a curtain of silky, shimmering veils, so light it is nearly weightless. Despite the insubstantial texture, it creates a barrier and I can go no further. Within these veils, the sound of an enchanting melody played on a flute comes forth and haunts me to my core, causing me to feel a surge of such intense and insistent yearning I can barely contain it. The music pulls on my heartstrings with its poignant lyricism. I imagine the magical coming of spring, a chorus of angels welcoming the soul home, the embrace of a long dead loved one I have not seen in years, the appearance of the rainbow after a time of lost hope. I know I must find the source of that sublime sound or I will die of longing for it.

As I look more closely with my newly anointed Eyes of Pure Love, a feminine form, so graceful and lovely it must be a Goddess, appears before me from within the veils. It's a woman, no, a bird, no, a butterfly, a whirling dervish, the spinning cosmos, the wheel of the year circling endlessly as the seasons change in rapid succession. All I know for certain is that there is a never-ending motion of an exotic dance of veils playing havoc with my mind.

The veils swirl like a turning kaleidoscope, ranging in color through the entire spectrum of the rainbow with all subtle gradations of shades in between. The image forms a tapestry that blends together in a mandala of intricate, ever-changing patterns. Turning and shifting, the pattern never settles but dances in a constant, mind boggling flux and flow of motion.

Without effort on my part I am inexorably drawn into this whirlwind of energy and I am embraced within the swirling, veils. At first the electrifying energy is unsettling and disorienting. The melody of the flute has turned wild and matches the dance of the veils, seductively insistent and pulsating in its rhythms. I feel this untamable, driving impulse as the life force behind my breath and the flow of my blood throughout my body. I feel more alive than ever before in my entire life.

But soon I feel the effects of a new unbearably sweet melody coming from the flute that calms me like a lullaby. The mood of the song has diametrically transformed and the motion of the veils matches it. A sensation like the rocking of a cradle or a gondola floating on gentle waters soothes me and I am at peace. Nothing is as it seems and I am lost forever and ever in an eternal dream, my rational mind asleep and unable to distinguish or care what is real. I am experiencing the mesmerizing illusion of the Goddess Maya.

She sings to me in a sweetly soft and seductive voice of pleasure gardens and groves of celestial joy. All the while, the melody of the flute continues in harmony with the song of the Goddess. Holding me tenderly within Her realm, I am lulled by Her voice of velvet, losing my will and the energy to proceed. I have become a tiny infant sheltered safely in the arms of the Divine Mother, cherished and adored. My eyes close and I cannot even begin to imagine wanting to resist. I want only to rest forever in this oasis of fantasy and peace. I am literally hypnotized and spellbound within the Veil of *Maya*, filled with a heady indolence like the inertia of a drug-in-duced haze. Floating in this intoxication of the senses, I lose all concept of time and space and am unable to rouse myself from this psychedelic dream.

But the flute is still calling me. The sound is no longer seductive and dreamy but bold and insistent, almost strident, as though trying to warn or awaken me. Underneath the heavy lethargy of pleasure, I am being coaxed and cajoled to come back to myself. I can hear the blue child calling me by name and somehow I can answer and remember who I am. The yearning for the Beloved of my Heart again overtakes my soul. I feel as though I have been awakened from a spell of enchantment by the flute, the child's voice, and the touch of his hand in mine. I remember now the reason why I am here. Abruptly, I am pulled beyond the veils and when I turn back for one last look they have vanished. In my heart, I know I have passed a testing, but I also know that I have been given the help of a god.

The blue boy is still holding my hand and has never for one moment let our connection drop. I can feel his profound love for me coming through his hand as a beacon of warmth and light guiding me on. I am brought into an intimate, miniature sanctuary, sensing only through my third eye. As I open my eyes, the interior is pitch black, like an overcast sky on a dark moon night. Cave like, it is so dark that all of my mundane senses fall away and I begin to see without sight, hear without sound, feel without touch. I feel disembodied, floating in a mysterious atmosphere like nowhere I have ever been before. There are no windows here and no source of light. It feels as though I am in a womb chamber making ready to come to birth.

The boy begins to light the many candles on an imposing stand-ing candelabra and now I notice other seekers are present, both musicians and devotees. Entranced by all the tiny, glowing flames of light, when I glance away for a brief moment to look at them my vision blurs and the boy has disappeared in a flash, leaving me alone. But I don't feel alone or lost without him for a marvelous, ce-lestial sound is surrounding me, the melody of loving voices joined in a devotional chant accompanied by a flute. And somehow the blue child is still with me, for the sweetness of his being has opened and filled me with his loving presence.

The doors of perception are being opened and my reality is totally altered. I have the distinct impression that I have been in this set-ting with this community of souls many times before. As I join in the chant, the words and the melody are familiar and well known to me. The Call of the Flute is leading me on, weaving its sinuous melody around the chant. Impossible as it seems, I can hear the sounds of water and gently murmuring waves surrounding me on all sides. And I smell the intoxicating, salty scent of the sea. Closing my eyes once more, I am open and ready to receive what comes to me.

9. <u>A Journey Through the Divine Eye</u>

Through the incessant pulse of the tabla, the hypnotic repetition of the drone, and the endless waves of the chant, I am slowly being pulled into a deep state of meditation.

Tiny brass bells are chiming and the drone of the harmonium begins to set a devotional mood. Led by a flute, the music starts out slowly and simply. As the melody rises and falls, voices join in to create subtle harmonies. Soon I too am singing the Sanskrit words as though I have always known them. The chant drones on and on and I become immersed in its endless rhythms.

The voices of the singers are like the *Gandharva*, those Celestial Singers of myth and legend whose melody is the aria of heaven. The Call of the Flute alternates with the magical voices leading us further into the spell. The lilting cadence of the Sanskrit names for God binds me in the rhythm of its *mantra*. I feel as though I am melting in the sweetness of this sublime melody. I am so utterly moved by the heavenly music and the poetic meter of the words that tears of joy are rolling soundlessly down my cheeks.

Soon I become aware of a Presence that I can feel with a palpable sense of physical reality. With my eyes still closed, I feel a gentle, wet nuzzling like a kiss on my forehead. A humid breath sultry as a tropical summer breeze wafts over my face. It is Surabhi, the Celestial Wish-Giving Cow. We have called Her to us by chanting the names of Krishna, Her companion and Protector. As a sign to me of Her significance, Surabhi wears the *Vanamali*, the garland of wild flowers and *tulasi*, an herb which is sacred to the Blue God. Garlanding me with Her *Vanamali*, she makes me ready for the journey I must take to find the Beloved. I have been marked by her kiss, giving me the ability to enter into a sacred realm.

Surabhi has come for me with a message but we cannot and need not speak in words in this sacred place. With her hypnotic gaze, she gently leads me into the center of her deep brown eyes. I feel disoriented, as though I am shrinking down to the size of a tiny, embryonic seed, the undiluted essence of me. Then I am pulled into the soft, warm, brown of those bovine eyes, all seeing, all knowing. I feel totally accepted for who I am. And I feel myself being drawn down and down, yearning, melting, full of reverence and awe into the Divine Eye of God.

Being in the Eye of Surabhi, the Emissary of Krishna, is warm and dark and womblike. In this complete stillness, the Call of the Flute floats and soars above me seeming to come from the very heart of God. I am surrounded by love and submerged in the salty amniotic fluid of the Eye/Womb of Surabhi, the Universal Mother of All Things. My body begins to take form from the tiny seed and slowly I grow into the full potential of who I am to be. I feel entirely calm, waiting to emerge into a new world. And I know all will come in its own time, in its own way, for I am about to be born, and it is exactly how it is meant to be. .

The chant continues, floating above me and I am blissfully out of body in the Land of *Nirvana*. Time passes, but I have completely lost touch with the linear movement of the minutes in favor of the absolute moment of the Now. I realize that I am experiencing the time before birth, which we humans forget or lose contact with in this life each time we come to be on earth. I have the sensation of being held in the arms of love, completely cared for and cherished. Floating in the womb, I am ensconced in eternal peace and bliss. I feel I could rest here forever. But I know that someone or something has been waiting for me to arrive and come to birth and is now calling me forth. As the chant subtly increases in volume and tempo, I feel pushed by a pulsating, inexorable energy that is becoming urgent and overwhelming. I can no longer rest in bliss, or return to where I was. I can only surrender to the motion that is moving me rapidly forward along this path towards the light.

10. <u>Murali, The Call of The Flute</u>

As the tempo and volume of the chant peak in a frenzy and explosion of sound waves, I am born abruptly into a Garden of Paradise. I feel a bubble bursting and float free of all barriers and restrictions, emerging like a butterfly from a protective cocoon into another existence. Tremulous and innocent as a new- born lamb, I am dazzled by the proliferation of sounds, scents, sights, and emotions that are bombarding my senses. But a Presence is here to greet and welcome me, calming me and gently showing me this new world. It is Surabhi the Sacred Mother Cow, Companion of Krishna, the Blue God of Love and Music.

I am in the forests of Vrindavana in Braj on the banks of the Yamuna River, thousands of years ago in an ancient time, under the full moon in the month of Shravana. And this idyllic grove is the secret Love Garden of the Lord Krishna. This place is an oasis far from the mundane world, where life exists in eternal play and delight. In this magical realm, no thought need be given to past or future, for life is lived to fulfill every dream in the here and now. Anything and everything is possible.

Tropical flowers are blooming, perfuming the atmosphere of this magical Grove. The vegetation glimmers and glows, saturated with the light of the full moon. The monsoon has come to refresh and renew the parched lands, and all is lush and verdant, heralding the impending arrival of Krishna, the Sovereign of this land. All the aspects of Nature have been heightened and enhanced as if painted in Technicolor by the Divine Master Painter. I have entered a Realm of Wonder and Delight.

Into the Grove, the animals of the woods gather and come closer together. The mellifluous sounds of the bangles and ankle bells ornamenting the *gopis*, the cowherd maidens who are the Lovers of God, chime softly in the air as they enter the forest. And I hear the distant sound of a flute.

This is the most auspicious night of the year, and it is my deep privilege to have been given the gift of being here now at this perfect moment. I am here to witness the *Rasa Lila*, the Mystic Love Dance of the Lord Krishna which brings His devotees divine communion and Oneness with All that is. Perhaps I will be called to join the Magic Circle at last, no longer an outsider. Perhaps this time, this once, the tragic dream of missed connection, of ultimate loss and eternal separation, can become a tale of love realized and longing fulfilled. I have joined the *satsang*, the community of devotees, to partake in the blessing of the Lord.

As a prelude and initiation to entering this Sacred Circle, Krishna has tested His devotees, the *gopis,* while they played in the Yamuna River by requiring them to come out of the water naked to retrieve the clothing He has stolen from them. And they trust and love the Blue God so completely that there is no desire to conceal any part of their being from Him. Afterwards, Krishna offers to grant their wish and bestow a boon. And so they have been promised that He will return on the full moon night of Shravana in the autumn to dance with them in the Mystic Rasa Lila.

For forty-one days now, since the stealing of the clothes, the *gopis* have been praying and making offerings at the shrine under the Sacred Kadamba Tree on the Yamuna River. Day after day they have been bringing offerings of flowers, incense, and sweet fruits to show their devotion. The *gopis* have made a sacred *vrata* or vow and fasted, sustaining themselves only on *prasad*, the sacred food offerings to the Divine One. They have recited the myriad names of the Lord over and over again until their minds have become still. They have sung the *kirtana* and *bhajans* of praise endlessly until their voices have become mere whispers. They have moved in the ancient patterns of the Temple Dance until they have left their bodies. And as they have worshipped, so they have become *bhaktas*, the Lovers of God, preparing their souls for communion with the Divine.

Tonight, under the full moon in the month of Shravana, a great hush descends upon the gathering as we await our blessed audience with the Blue God. There is an intense outpouring of emotion among the devotees in their yearning for the Divine One. Many are weeping, though not in sorrow, for this suspended moment of stillness is so precious and the anticipation so great. And then the haunting sounds of the flute begin to reach our ears, coming closer, echoing the song in our hearts. It is Murali, the Flute of Irresistible Attraction, calling us to Krishna.

11. <u>Krishna Manamohan,</u> <u>The Enchanter of Hearts</u>

Of all the tones that vibrate in the many hued dream of the world, this one note from Krishna's flute can be heard as the Call of the Infinite. It awakens the harmonies of the soul creating a passionate love and yearning that can melt even the most diffident heart. The melody is at once plaintive and languorous, uplifting as joyous laughter yet full of tears, mesmerizing as a charmed snake, and radiant as new love. It is an extension of the unworldly beauty of Krishna Himself.

The honeyed melody draws us inexorably to Him, for once it begins, no one and nothing can resist the call of the Mystic Flute Player, Krishna Manamohan, the Enchanter of Hearts. He is calling us to return to the Land of Our Souls. The music summons us, insisting that all else be forgotten, inviting us to enter The Dance. All other sounds pale before this one. Never in all my life have I heard such an exquisitely sublime sound.

When the Blue God appears we are breathtaken by His ravishing beauty. His face is luminous as the full moon, His lotus eyes are large and gleaming, His lips red as berries. His smile embraces us with warmth, full of the promise of never ending happiness. He is garlanded in the sacred blossoms and *tulasi* of the God, crowned with peacock feathers, and wears the *Kundala*, the crocodile earrings of the Lord. His sheer grace is beyond anything in the universe, for Krishna is the Arouser of the Desire of the World. His luminous spirit makes the entire cosmos sparkle with vitality. When we are in the presence of the Blue God, we can concentrate on nothing else. And yet, despite the intensity of our awe, He is fully human to our eyes.

Krishna has taken the *tribhanga*, the triple bended *asana* or posture of benevolent tranquility. We become filled with bliss watching His swaying movements. Blowing into His flute with the sweet nectar of His breath, the sound flows from Him, intoxicated, intoxicating. We adore Him beyond all things. And He has come into His body to delight us, as the expression of God's love for humanity. He is here for the sole purpose of giving and receiving joy as both the Lover and the Beloved.

As Krishna the Divine Musician plays His heavenly melody, the entire appearance of nature begins to change and coalesce, to meld and merge, until we can see beyond the *maya* of separation that All is One. Everything is woven together into one exquisite tapestry by the strains of His celestial music. The notes are soaring and vibrating like a symphonic poem, echoing through all of space to the abode of the Gods and Goddesses in *nirvana*. Something extraordinary and supernatural is taking place as all things begin to reflect the beauty and rapture of their true nature.

Krishna moves to the Center of the Grove and the *gopis* form a ring, like a charmed circle, around Him. All of eternity is contained in this magic Circle. There is no beginning or end and all are equal here without class or *caste*. As the *gopis* clasp hands, the energy flows round and round binding them together in the Web of Life. The enchanting music of Murali continues, accompanied by the chiming of ornaments as they begin to move in the Great Circle Dance of Love, the Eternal Cosmic Dance between God and His Lovers.

The movement of the Dance is both exhilarating and entrancing, for all who partake are spellbound by the Blue God. The difficulties and sorrows of daily existence are forgotten in His presence and all rejoice in the fullness of life. The Lord asks nothing except our complete surrender to the eternal rhythms of the Dance of Life. There is nothing else in existence except the Dance, the sound of the flute, the pull of the divine, and The Lord. All is in motion, moving inexorably toward union and ecstasy.

Krishna's beloved consort is Radha. She is Krishna's other self,

His Eternal Companion, for He has divided His Oneness in two so He may experience the fullness of His love through union with His other half. They dance and celebrate one another, joining hand to hand, heart to heart creating all life in the universe. But the other *gopis* love Krishna as well, and so He multiplies himself over and over, creating a Krishna for each one. Each maiden is enveloped in a misty cloud of sensuous blue velvet, in a world all her own. At the same time, He is still at the center of the Circle creating the music that moves the Cosmos, captivating our hearts. For each *gopi*, He is the only Krishna, hers alone. God dances with all His lovers, anywhere, everywhere, in all times and places. *Maya*, the Goddess of Illusion, conceals the true divinity of Krishna from the *Bhaktas*, so that His sweetness and humanity can be experienced even more fully. He is every Seeker's heart of desire; He is everything to all, the essence of overflowing joy.

12. <u>Dwarapala, the Guardian of the Portal</u>

But for me, I am only a spectator to this fantastical dance, frozen within myself and unable to move forward. Though I am filled with an aching desire and the deepest longing to join the circle, I still feel the barriers and obstacles of my nightmare of limitations. I am waiting to be called, unable to take the incentive to move forward, despairing that I will always be an outsider. It feels as though there is some invisible Guardian at the portal of the circle judging me.

At first this presence seems to be only a ferocious stone *Dwarapala*, the traditional statue that guards the entrance of all temples. But as I gaze at the terrifying Gatekeeper, he becomes unquestionably real. Standing before me is a handsomely dressed, mustached man with a jeweled turban who looks like a prince. His face is angry and frightening, his physical posture, imposing and forbidding. He is arrogant, haughty, and cruelly cold in his demeanor towards me. As he leers at me, I am hypnotized by the intrusive intensity of his gaze, my body and blood frozen like a tiny, timid rabbit before a rearing cobra. He sneers at me, mocking me as unworthy to enter this sacred space. Screaming at me to depart, he pushes me violently away. He is holding a flaming sword in each hand and I can feel the terrible heat of the fire scorching my skin. Walking the perimeter of the circle, he creates a barrier of hellish proportion and temperature out of the flames. No one can possibly cross over and survive.

I allow myself to be diminished and made small. As the Guardian continues to taunt and curse me, I begin to cry and shrink into myself. I am becoming a mere shadow of who I really am. I grow smaller and smaller, dwindling in stature until soon I will be only a tiny teardrop of loss and despair. I can imagine even that minute tear, the last bit of the precious sweetness of my life and hope, burning in the flames and drying up into a grain of salt with only bitterness left. And then, all will be lost. Time stands still, as the universe waits to see how I will respond.

Suddenly without warning, an aggressive energy like a fierce mother bear protecting her young slaps me across my face, awakening me abruptly without mercy from my nightmare. It is not a hard or painful blow but it stings, jolting me out of my somnolent and victimized state of acceptance. For I have been in shock from this terrifying vision.

I remember now how the Gypsy asked me three times if I would accept and embrace my destiny with my entire being. I hear her words again and her confidence in me, "all will be well no matter how it may seem."

Rediscovering the power and integrity of my spirit, I begin to fight for my life's dream. I can't believe that I could possibly allow anyone or anything to stop me now or keep me from my Beloved after I have traveled so far. I recall the words of the Gypsy Crone as she placed the amulet around my neck and I hold on to my talisman as though it is the sole connection to my heart's desire and to my very life. Memories and images begin to form for me and I become aware of all the extraordinary events I have already experienced. I remember the joy of sharing purple plums with the Blue Child, I feel the compassion of Surabhi the Sacred Cow, I hear again the Call of the Flute, I see the *gopis* dancing and beckoning me to enter the Circle of Love, I behold the beautiful face of God crowned with peacock feathers. And I am uplifted and renewed.

With a flash of insight I understand that the forbidding Guardian is my own creation, my inner demon. There is no one here to stop me except myself and my own inner critics and judges. I realize I can vanquish this limiting presence with the strength of my will, through the power of my love, and with the help of my allies. I feel the supportive presence of the Gypsy Crone, Surabhi the Sacred Cow, and the Blue Child surrounding me in complete unity and harmony.

Using deep concentration and determination, I begin to unknot the tangled web of illusion I have bound myself with. The amulet of the dark skinned flute player begins to glow, warming and unthawing my frightened heart. The purity of my love slowly starts to over-whelm and dissolve the intimidating image. Chanting a *mantra* of power, I start to feel a strength of purpose within myself and know that I am truly deserving of the blessings of the Eternal Beloved; it is my birthright.

I begin to grow in stature until I am as majestic and firmly rooted in the earth as an imposing tree. I have become the Tree of Life, a vessel for all the beautiful and healing energies of growth within the sacred life force. I am in my body once again, becoming the temple of a glorious and compelling Goddess. I am invincible. Nothing and no one can stop me.

As my self-imposed spell shatters and breaks apart, it loses its hold on me. I take in one deep inhalation and breathe out in a tremen-dous spurt of energy. The power of the angry, threatening prince is annihilated in one breath. He drops the flaming swords in anguish as though he has been burned. Combined with the strength of my breath, my one tiny tear, the drop of salty fluid coming from the well of my despair, is enough to extinguish the raging flames. The fire is completely contained and quelled, doing no harm. The prince looks utterly bewildered, unbelieving and shocked that I would dare to stand up to his vitriolic wrath.

As though exorcised, the force of his negativity blows out of the top of his head spewing forth in an explosion of black, putrid fumes. The expression of hatred and disdain on his face disintegrates and is replaced with a look of defeat and then complete indifference. He is nothing but an empty shell, an illusion of an inner demon whose portrait I have created through my lack of faith. I begin to feel compassion for him, for he is, after all, my own creation and part of me. And so I ask him what he wants, what he needs from me to be at peace.

Looking into his face, I see the deep brown of the prince's eyes start to fill and brim over with tears as he cries great sobs of relief and release. All he really wants is the love and acceptance I have always craved for myself believing there was never enough. But in Krishna's Circle, love is endless and overflowing. Once the prince understands this simple truth, fed and nourished with *prema*, he is free to be who and what he truly is. As if being released from a spell, he begins to transform into a beautiful white Mother Cow with the loving and compassionate eyes of a Divine Being. It is Surabhi, the faithful companion of Krishna, come to welcome me to the Inner Circle. She is my ally, disguised as the Trickster, and is here to grant my heart's deepest wish. It is all a part of the *lila*, the divine play of the Blue God.

Surabhi reminds me that there in one final testing and I hear again the words of the Gypsy Crone. I must hang from Asvattha, the Tree of Life, giving up my allies, my strength, and my will. I must surrender from the depths of my soul all that I am in order to be in the presence of the Divine One. I must come before the Eternal Beloved utterly alone and unadorned. I agree and vow to withhold no part of my being, to become one of the *gopis*, as Surabhi leads me into the Circle.

13. <u>Dyed in Hari's Color</u>

I will fasten the bells of his love to my feet

And dance in front of Girdhar,

Dancing and dancing I will please his eyes;

My love is an ancient one.

My love is the only truth.

I cannot forget, even for a moment

The beauty of my lover.

I am dyed in Hari's colour.

(#16 Kurl 40)

Waiting for me at the perimeter of the Circle, Krishna stands under a tree which seems to be upside down. As I step under the shelter of the root/branches, I feel as though I am being turned head over heels inside out. I am not afraid as I surrender all I thought I was and all I thought I desired, giving everything up to God. Suddenly I am literally hanging upside down from the tree and my vision of life is changed diametrically and completely forever. I am fully aware that He is God. All things are possible for this is the mythic *Asvattha* the Gypsy spoke of. I am about to experience the flowering of my highest potential. In an instant, the tree blossoms luxuriantly and begins to produce fruit. And as the sacred fruits of the *Asvattha* ripen, they turn a deep blue purple hue like the color of the Divine One's skin.

Krishna comes to me and He nods with pleasure at the amulet around my neck. I notice that unlike the many- armed Hindu deities I am familiar with, He has only two arms and looks completely human and approachable. And I am struck by the similarity of the Blue God's wondrous countenance to the image on my talisman. I remember to feel its energy close to my heart as the Gypsy instructed me. "Who are you?" I ask in wonder. And He says "I am the Beloved of All, the One you have always longed for yet already know deep in your heart." Hearing these words, everything in the entire universe is at peace and in harmony and I am once again standing upright.

Now I know that the tragedy and sorrow of my dream of lost connections is being healed and transformed in this very moment. The memory of the pain and despair of the dream allows me to experience this ultimate connection with an even greater depth of gratitude. The frantic urge to grasp and grab onto something precious and unattainable is over forever.

I am bursting with the longing to be with my Eternal Beloved. My heart is expanding with the pure essence of love that flows back and forth to and from Krishna in endless waves. I have not forgotten the Gypsy's words and I pick some of the fruit, the deep purple blue plums. Tasting several, I offer the sweetest one to the radiant and smiling Lord. He accepts my offering. Looking deeply into my eyes, He sees into my innermost being as I stand alone before Him. I see myself reflected in His eyes like a mirror. And in His eyes I am able to see what He sees and I look upon myself as divine. I allow the last remnants of my roles, protections, and illusions to fall away and become fully who I am meant to be, my own true self.

The Blue God extends His hand to me and everything stops for one endless moment. My seeking and yearning is fulfilled in the simple joining of our hands. Without any need for language, He expresses the profundity of His love for me through His compassionate eyes and smile, bringing me into the Rasa Dance. Tears of joy, like precious pearls from the salty sea, roll silently down my face, releasing and washing away all the sorrows of the past.

With tenderness, He holds my soul in His hands, as I enter into the center of the Sacred Circle. I feel the velvet blueness of the skin of His cheek brushing against mine, offering me the eternal Embrace of Deep Peace. A chord of rapturous joy arises in me as I receive His *shaktipat*, the nectar of His essence, my awakening. The cells of my being are rearranging, splitting like atoms, creating something new, and vibrant, and whole. Everything beautiful that was lost is found again, all endings become new beginnings, old doors close and new ones open, and all the infinite potential and possibility of life are reborn. The frozen Waters of Life break free and begin to thaw in a roaring release of energy as the barrenness of the desert gives way to the green, singing joy of springtime.

I feel Krishna's touch bringing forth the hidden music of my soul. The sweetness of His embrace melts away all aches and pains, heals all hurts, sorrows, and losses, and makes all that is closed and restricted blossom into its highest potential. Through the magic of His touch, the mere joining of our hands, my hair becomes pure strands of glistening silk, my skin as smooth as satin, my form as lovely as a Goddess. The inner divinity that was curled up and silent within me begins to unfurl in undiminished splendor.

The *gopis* open their arms and welcome me in as a sister. We clasp hands to reform the Circle and I feel the energy of the community of *bhaktas* flowing through me as I help to create the unbreakable ring of never ending love. I become an essential link in this beautiful chain of devotion. There is one especially radiant *gopi* who stands out amidst the gathering. I have heard her soulful voice singing above all the others and. she attracts me deeply. Our gazes lock in recognition across the circle and she comes to stand beside me, grasping my hands as a friend and companion on the Path. "Who are you?" I ask. "I am Mirabai." "Such a beautiful name" I answer. She tells me we will meet again; " my journey is the path you will follow. This you will see in the fullness of time." And the Dance begins anew.

The tempo and energy of the music gradually takes on an urgency as the heartbeat of its rhythm crescendos to a peak and reverberates throughout my entire body. The flute no longer sounds like a recognizable melody and has been transformed into resounding and sonorous exclamations of joy. Coiled at the base of my root *chakra*, the *kundalini* or serpent power shoots upward through the top of my head exploding my mind into the universe. My entire being is in *samadhi*, the ecstasy of the gods. In the background, the triumphal song of Murali proclaims our awakening to the Divine: "I am the melody and He is the words; I am the words and He is the melody." We are entwined in the rapture of the Dance of Life. All is One.

Now I know that my Eternal Beloved will always be with me just as He is present in the hearts of all His devotees. We are all merged and floating in the Ocean of Bliss, all the *gopis*, all the Krishnas, all of nature, all of me. As His essence infiltrates us, we become dusky and blue skinned, dyed in Hari's color. We are all permeated with the divinity of His love; and imbued with His eternal spirit. I hear the *gopis* chanting: "Kanu bina gita nahi," without Krishna there is no song. "

When the morning finally comes, the sun rises in glory to reflect the evening's ecstatic celebration. Krishna says, "Now my Beloved, look into my mouth and you will see the entire universe, just as I once showed Mother Yasoda when I was a child." To my astonishment, as He opens His mouth, I see all the worlds that ever were and ever will be. I am literally swallowed whole and I pass through the blue of the Lord's inner recesses as if He was an open door.

And a new tale begins.

PART II, Development:
The Legend of Mirabai

1. The Incarnation of a *Gopi*

When in spiritual bliss, people often say "God is in my heart, God is my thoughts." But this extraordinary experience of being inside the consciousness of the Blue God is something far different in nature. I am literally in the heart of God, in the mind of God, seeing through His eyes. Disembodied and floating above the scene, I can feel every emotion of the human drama that is beginning to unfold before me. Through Krishna's omnipotence, I am able to become one with each personality in the tale I am being called to witness. Although puzzled about why and how I am in this time and place being shown this particular life, there is no time for reflection, for once again I have the uncanny sensation that I am about to be born as pulsating, pushing energies move me through the birth canal.

It is 1498 in Rajasthan, the Land of Kings, in Northern India. A queen is laboring to bring new life into the world, for a daughter is being born into the noble House of Rathore. Around the Rani's neck is an amulet of protection and blessing, depicting a Dark-skinned Flute Player. I can feel the powerful birth pangs of the mother and the child's astonishment as she is thrust into life with her first

66

glimpse of the world.

When the infant finally emerges after an extended and difficult labor, she is blue from the long struggle. It becomes so real that I am gasping with her as she takes her first breath. Quickly, the midwife briskly rubs her body and the natural color returns to the child's complexion. I feel a primal connection with this newly born being, as if she were a part of me or I a part of her. Drawn into this tiny infant's spirit, I see the world through her eyes as something new and precious. Realizing that I am this little soul but still myself from another time is an unsettling blend of feeling split in two yet united in a wholeness. I remember hearing people talk of recalling past life memories and wonder if I am receiving this phenomenal insight from the Blue God.

As the mother looks into her child's eyes for the first time, she remembers the prophecy surrounding her conception, that her birth is the gift of Lord Krishna and she belongs to Him. And she sees the Dark One's blue color still imprinted upon her daughter's face and form. Seeing through Krishna's Divine Eye and His supreme mind, I know His deep pleasure in witnessing a new devotee coming forth on earth. The child is named Mirabai, "One Whose Countenance Kindles like the Sun." The royal priest/astrologer, comes later to bless the birth and predicts a remarkable future for the child, something connected to music. He says that at the moment of Mira's birth, there was an unusual starburst in the sky and he knows that a special spiritual incarnation has manifested on earth.

The child's family is Vaishnavi, worshippers of Vishnu in His many incarnations. But Mira will go far beyond this tradition into the Path of *Bhakti* for Krishna, Vishnu's eighth incarnation. Her name will be remembered for centuries as a poet, musician, and devotee, and also as a rebel, a non-traditionalist, and a woman of great courage. Some say she was an incarnation of the gopi milkmaiden Radha, consort of Krishna. Others wonder if she was Saraswati returned to grace us with Her music. Legends surround her and facts are few. Perhaps she was a Goddess unknown to those whose lives she graced.

2. <u>Queen's Desire</u>

For the Rajah and the Rani of Merwer, Mira's birth is a miracle of faith and a much longed for blessing. Unable to conceive, the Queen receives a message while deep in meditation and prayer. She hears a voice murmuring in her mind, telling her that she must consult the old Gypsy Crone, Matriarch of the Bhilani Tribe, who frequents a secluded oasis in the desert. This famed Seer uses the ancient oracle of the tarot to divine the future. Perhaps if they travel there, she will be at rest from her endless wanderings and will read their destiny for them.

The royal couple takes the long journey in an entourage, riding in a luxurious covered litter on the back of an elephant. A caravan of camels and many attendants accompany them. Reclining on soft, embroidered pillows, the Rajah and Rani whisper together with affection and excitement about the prospects of their travel. Their every comfort is attended to and there are frequent stops to picnic, enjoy the ponds, and relax. Music, poetry, and dance are performed at the rest stops and there is endless singing and chanting, both sacred and secular as the procession of the caravan advances.

I see this expedition through the Divine Eye of Krishna, for it is He who designs this *kismet* or destiny. Already I feel at ease in this new role as a Watcher of the Sacred Tale, accepting that I am here for a yet unknown reason without questioning the experience. I am completely open and enthralled seeing this plot unfold before my eyes almost as though I am watching a stage play. But at the same time, it is a play that involves and moves me so deeply as if it were my own life. And then it becomes my own life and I am lost in the story, no longer an onlooker but a full participant in all that is unfolding before my eyes.

After a long journey, the royal couple arrives at the oasis to ask their questions and seek the advice of the Wise One. They find the Seer sitting quietly under a tree heavily laden with dark blue plums, as though their arrival is expected. She is wearing an amulet with an image of the Dark-skinned Flute Player at its center. Hearing her voice, the Rani recognizes it from her meditation as the voice inside her mind.

The Seer motions to a brightly painted vardo, her home on wheels. Surrounding the sides of the door, a pair of exquisite peacocks are painted, guarding the entrance. The sides of the wagon are decorated with auspicious signs. An upward pointing open hand gives protection and blessing, and in the palm is the All Seeing Eye of God. Various *mandalas* and sacred *yantras* are also painted everywhere, making the wagon into a tiny temple of divinity. The Gypsy

Crone invites the Queen into her wagon, but tells her husband, the Rajah, he must remain outside. Reluctantly, he agrees and the door is closed, the shutters drawn.

Once inside, the Gypsy Queen lights candles and they sit at a low table made like an altar. After the proper rituals and offerings have been made, the Rani is told to shuffle a deck of tarot cards and when she feels ready, cut them into three piles, facing down. She must turn over the top card of each group for her destiny to be told. Drawing the first one, she sees the face of the Hanged Man, the Seeker who sets out on the Path of Life and must turn herself inside out and upside down to find her heart's desire, sacrificing all that she is. Then she sees the Wheel of Life, the *Mandala* Journey, the ever- turning circle of coming and going which the Traveler must follow. And last the World, a Queen with the stature of a goddess who holds the universe in the palm of her hand. She is the image of the Rani herself and symbolizes the end of all desire and the manifestation of the dreams in one's soul. The outcome shows the Queen her heart's desire but the Gypsy sees in the cards a sacrifice and a journey ahead before her wish can be granted.

The Crone tells her that there is a daughter in her waiting to be conceived, but that only the dark skinned flute player, *Avatar* of Vishnu, can grant this boon and bring it to fruition. They must go on pilgrimage to Braj, the sacred lands of Krishna, renouncing their royalty for the duration, traveling like simple peasants, walking barefoot, hand in hand, the entire way without the customary luxuries of the ruling class. The instructions are explicit and must be followed to the letter, like some Sacred Law of the Universe that cannot be broken, questioned, or changed in any way. This is the sacrifice of the Hanged One. Once she has arrived, she is cautioned that part of her sacrifice means that she must follow the path alone, unaccompanied.

Following the Ban Yatra , the pilgrimage of the Twelve Forests that is shown in the Wheel of Fortune, they must arrive on the night of the Sacred Circle Dance, for only on this night can the Blue God be found by all seekers. There in the heart of the forest the Rani will find *Asvattha*, the mythic Wish Fulfilling Tree. It will appear to be upside down and under that sacred tree with blue leaves stands the portal to her heart's desire. If the couple can gain entrance into the Rasa Lila of the Blue God and dance in His honor, their wish will be granted, the blessings of the World card.

She warns the Queen with one last prediction: the child she bears will never truly belong to her, but she will say no more. And as they leave, the Crone removes her amulet placing it over the Rani's head, telling her to keep it close to her heart. The Queen is told that the amulet must be passed on to yet another devotee as an offering after she has gained her heart's desire.

3. <u>The Blessing of Lord Krishna</u>

The King and Queen undertake this arduous pilgrimage according to all stipulations. Never tiring, they are filled with supreme hope and faith in their quest as they walk the Ban Yatra. At the exact auspicious moment specified by the old Gypsy, they enter into the center of the forest in Braj. A stately mother cow approaches to greet and welcome them. It is the Surabhi, the Sacred Companion of Krishna. Surabhi anoints the Queen's eyes with the precious essence of *prema-netra* which affects her like a magic potion. Then she is led away from the Raja to face her destiny alone. It is no small matter to face God.

As the Rani smells the sweet perfume of this mystic elixir, she feels her vision being magnetically drawn into the warm, brown eyes of the bovine Mother. She can see into the eye womb of the Sacred Cow and enters into a deep trance in the still time before conception, where all things are possible. In the amniotic waters, she can see the seed of a tiny perfect girl child waiting for her, waiting to be conceived, waiting to be awakened and born. I am experiencing with the Queen this exquisite surrender to destiny as I find somehow a hidden piece of myself in her vision.

In this other worldly state, The Rani is taken by Surabhi into the center of a sacred grove where a tree with leaves as dark blue as Krishna's skin stands, appearing to be upside down. She hears the sound of a flute calling to her. The music is so expressive and mesmerizing that she forgets everything else in the world as though under a spell. As I watch, I wonder, where have I heard this marvelous melody before? Looking more closely the Queen sees the Dark One Himself waiting for her under the tree, blending into the dense canopy of blue leaves, flowers, and plums. Crowned with peacock feathers, His dazzling beauty takes her breath away. He is smiling at her in welcome with radiant warmth. No words need to be exchanged, for the Blue God knows the secret wishes of every devotee's heart.

Krishna tells the Rani that He is the portal to her heart's most deeply cherished dream. She kneels in reverence at His feet and with one touch of His hand on the top of her head at the crown *chakra*, He gives her the blessings of motherhood. The Rani's womb is opened for the gestation of a beautiful girl child. Without words it is understood that the child will belong to Krishna, that she has been His before, that she will be His in every rebirth.

After offerings and prayers, the royal couple is called by the enchanting music of Murali into the Great Circle Dance. The Rajah and Rani dance together in a rapture and ecstasy of devotion, feeling the magic of a divine blue presence embracing them both. Upon returning home, they find that their request has been granted.

This is the favorite story that the King and Queen tell their cherished daughter Mira each year on her birthday, saying over and over again that she is a gift from the Lord Krishna. Mira never tires of hearing about the magical events surrounding her conception and birth. From a young age, she begins begging her parents to take her on the pilgrimage of the Ban Yatra too. The Rajah and Rani promise her that they will make this journey together when the time is right.

The workings of God's fate cannot be questioned, and the couple is blessed with no other children. Mira is often solitary. But she has a special friend, a charming, dimpled boy with skin the color of deep blue plums, who shares her daily joys and sorrows. Mira's friend has a companion who is always close to him, a white mother cow with deep brown eyes. Mira tells her parents about the many extraordinary adventures she shares with her friends, for the boy and his pet have abilities beyond what can be believed. He is so much fun, full of endless imagination and play, and he is especially fond of butter. The cow allows them to ride together on her back and they go to many magical places. Her parents smile indulgently at her tales, for they have never seen the boy or his pet. For them, he is only an imaginary playmate that many children create, and most outgrow. But Mira says, "He's mine alone!"

4. <u>Raidas the *Chamar*</u>

Come, Charmer of Hearts,

For your speech is sweet.

O Krishna, did you ever rightly value

My childhood love?

Without Your sight I feel no ease,

My mind swings this way and that.

Mira says: I am Yours.

I will proclaim this, with Your permission,

To the beat of a drum.

(#100 Alston 75)

Some years later, Raidas the *chamar*, a leather worker of the untouchable *caste*, is having dreams and visions. Despite his lowly position in this lifetime, known to only a select few, he is a revered sage, a *guru*. Last night while dreaming, he envisioned all of his disciples deeply asleep except for a woman who was alone in Madhuban, the Forest of Sweetness. He has never seen her before and does not know her name, but he is compelled to search for her. For once he has seen her luminous face he is drawn inexorably to be in her presence.

In his dream, just as the full moon rises in the month of Shravrana, on the night of the *Rasa Lila*, he finds her. Raidas knows she has left behind a royal life of comfort and become persecuted because of his teachings. But she is immersed in bliss, in contemplation of the Lord Krishna, and she does not realize his presence. He hears celestial music, poetry and melodies of unimaginable beauty coming from deep within her being. And though her body is in silent meditation, still as a statue, he can see her soul dancing with Krishna, as though they were always meant to be together.

Now Raidas is traveling the endless sands of the Thar, searching and seeking. Something draws him, like a soul coming home to the Beloved. The sands of the desert are scorching under his feet; the heat is relentless, harsh, unforgiving. His mind is confused by the shifting illusions and shimmering mirage of the Thar until he is following blindly on faith alone to the destination his *karma* takes him to. A beautiful voice in his mind, singing in harmony with a flute, is his guiding light.

The hardships matter not, for Raidas is on a journey of the most solemn import. With him he carries his sacred *murti* of Krishna, the image he has kept close for as long as he can remember. This statue has come down to Raidas from his *guru* through the teachings of his lineage. Using *mantra*, prayer, and incantation, it has been imbued with the essence of the Lord. It is a beautiful life-like depiction of the Blue God crowned with peacock feathers, holding

His sacred flute to His lips. The *murti* is so realistic Raidas can hear the marvelous flute music in his mind whenever he holds the statue to his heart in prayer. Sometimes he even hears a message in words coming from the lips of the Blue God.

At the House of Rathore in Rajasthan, a wandering ascetic comes to the gate asking for alms. He is welcomed in, for the family is devoted to Vishnu. Mira, the young princess, is called by her mother to greet and serve the *swami* or holy man. In Mira's eyes, Raidas appears as a kindly old grandfather, not an astute or forbidding renunciate as he seems to some who encounter him. His gentle melodious voice, kindhearted smile, and tender manner give Mira a deep trust in him on first sight and she opens her loving nature to him in return. He calls her "beta" or darling child and says she is a little Radha. For Raidas, there is an immediate recognition of a soul who is the archetypal *bhakta*. He thinks, "This child is the woman of my dream; I can see in her the seed of what she will become."

Mira is enchanted with the *murti* of Krishna. The image reminds her of her cherished childhood companion. And like any young child will, she asks the sage if she may hold it. Raidas gives her the statue to care for while he is with them and instructs her in the *puja*. Mira cares for Krishna as a mother would treat her darling child, as a wife would honor her beloved husband, or as a friend would treat a special companion. She bathes and feeds Him, sings songs, dances for Him, and watches over Him tenderly with selfless devotion, confiding all of her innocent dreams in Him.

When it is time to bring *prasad* for the Blue God, there is a bowl of dark blue plums with skins of velvet among the offerings. Mira begins to taste each morsel carefully. In shock, her watching family starts to intervene for in orthodox Hindu worship the food is meant only for the Divine and is never eaten by the devotee before it has been sanctified by God. Raidas smiles calmly at the proceedings and asks Mira to explain herself. She tells him that she wants to be certain the food is the very best, most delicious offering before feeding it to her Beloved Krishna. Raidas nods with pleasure at Mira's insightful and loving heart. His acknowledgment and approval set her firmly on the Path of *Bhakti.*

Each morning and evening Mira sits with Raidas at the family shrine, absorbing his teachings. He shows her how to hold the *murti* to her heart *chakra* so she too can hear the sacred flute music. Mira is enthralled by the enchanting melodies and sings along effortlessly with a natural responsiveness that is unusual in so young a child. For Raidas, this is the sign of her highly awakened spiritual nature and the musical potential she carries within. And he tells her that if she remains pure of heart in her devotion she may even hear a message coming from the lips of the *murti*. Already she knows that Raidas is her Divine Master.

.

5. <u>Yellow as an Autumn Leaf</u>

The link between me and Shyam cannot be broken.

I went yellow as the autumn leaf

And the people thought I had jaundice.

My father sent for the doctor

Who felt my pulse.

It was my heart that was breaking,

But the doctor did not know the secret.

My Lord, Mira is distressed in your absence,

Come and grant her your sight!

(#72 Alston 63)

The time comes when Raidas the *chamar* must leave to continue his wanderings. He knows he has planted a seed and nurtured a tiny germinating bud in Mira which will flower into an extraordinary being in time. When he asks for the *murti* back, she is heartbroken, devastated, beyond consolation. It has become as essential to her well- being as the air she breathes. After Raidas leaves, she begins sobbing and pulls off all of her royal jewelry throwing it on the floor in a fit of pique. Wailing, she tells her mother that the statue has winked at her and told her a special secret. And now she cannot possibly live without Krishna's dazzling smile.

For days after the *guru's* departure, Mira cries endlessly, refuses to

83

eat, to sleep, to care for herself, to sing. She appears to be fever-ish, sick in both mind and body, pining away for love of the Dark God. Without Krishna, there is no joy left in her world. All the color and vitality have drained out of her life like spilled blood. Mira feels devitalized as though turned to stone and all things that were once vibrantly colorful are how flat and empty in shades of lifeless grey.

That night the young Mira has an ominous dream, a nightmare that will recur whenever she feels separated from her Lord Krishna. In the dream, she is trudging through something thick and hot under a devastating sun. It is the parched and desolate desert sands of the Thar. She walks, step after step, in an endless procession but makes no progress or semblance of forward motion. It feels as though she is pushing against a thick impenetrable barrier, which makes each step require overwhelming energy. The goal is beyond her reach and no matter how hard she tries, she cannot find Him. I recognize this dream as one of my own and I too am trapped in the nightmare.

Exhausted, her feet sink down into quicksand and she is trapped in the brutal harshness of the desert. She feels herself drying up, cell by cell, from lack of the precious moisture of the Waters of Life. In the dream, Mira withers up and turns to dust, to be blown away and intermingled with the innumerable grains of sand of the desert, lost forever in the endless horizon of the Thar. The dream holds her in a coma-like state of limbo and she is unable to awaken and return to her life. When I force myself to separate from Mira's dream, I am filled with despair and horror seeing her lifeless figure lying so still on the bed.

At the same moment of Mira's anguished nightmare, Raidas has a haunting and startling experience in his temple during *puja*. His beloved *murti* of Krishna begins to shed tears of grief. The garlands, jewels, and peacock feathers he uses to decorate and honor Krishna fall off the statue as if rejected; the candles lit for *arati* are blown out, extinguished by a fierce inhuman breath, and the temple darkens as though a storm was approaching.

Praying for an answer to the meaning of this strange omen, Raidas has a vision. This is no dream or hallucination. The Blue God begins playing His flute and underneath the tones Raidas hears His message, His wish. The melody is filled with grief and despair like the wailing of an inconsolable child. The Dark One tells him he must return in haste to the House of Rathore and give the child Mira the *murti*. Krishna says that He belongs to her, that she belongs to Him, and Raidas must follow His command.

Now Raidas hears the pulsating rhythm of a drum sounding like a feverish heartbeat and the voice of a young girl lamenting, pleading. Wrenched by the intensity of the pain and the loss that he hears; he knows he must journey quickly. Once more he travels the sands of the Thar, but this time he is fully aware of that which he seeks, the young Lady Mira.

When Raidas arrives, he places the murti in her hands and sits by the bedside of the princess for hours, chanting *mantras* of healing and return. In her deep coma, she can faintly hear him calling her back as if from some great distance, for the realm she has entered is far from the world of the living. Over and over, she hears the many names of Krishna being sung, Shyam, Kanha, Giridhara, Keshava, Gopala, Madan, Hari. Witnessing the scene, I join in the chanting, my heart in my throat, fearing for this lost part of myself. Slowly but surely Raidas unbinds the tangled knot of despair that is holding Mira captive and feeds her with the fruits of his love. And she begins to feel herself being called back to this world. The presence of the Blue God is there too, hovering behind Raidas, for those who have the eyes to see.

Deep within her coma, Mira feels a sensation of warmth and wetness nudging and licking her forehead and face. Compassionate brown eyes are gazing at her with intensity and purpose. It is Surabhi, the Companion of Krishna. As though in a spell, Mira is drawn into the eye of the Sacred Cow and held in a state of healing bliss in the amniotic waters. In this Eye of the Womb she feels her old self dissolving into the pure essence of the seed of life before gestation, regressing back into a time before life began. There is a new being coming to birth. The liquid fluidity of this wondrous mois- ture counteracts the dry, barrenness of the desert and she is slowly renewed. Immersed in this healing bath, Mira has found an ally, a guide, and a protector in Surabhi. The Wish Fulfilling Cow reminds her that she can come to her for solace in any time of need. Mira needs only to ask and the call will be answered.

Soon Mira is attracted by a melody full of yearning and joy. The sweet sound of the flute is calling her. The Blue God takes her hand drawing her back to life. Eventually, after many days, she awakens. But something is transformed forever in the cells of her body and Mira is no longer who she was. Her ability to see into the spiritual world has been altered beyond recognition. I too have been trans- formed for I am no longer the narrator or onlooker of this tale, but fully immersed in it as it becomes my own story.

When Raidas offers Mira the *murti*, the broken fragments of her heart which were scattered on the floor like her discarded jewelry are healed and made whole by this gift of generosity. As he leaves he tells her, "Remember me, *beta*, as I will remember you, for we will meet again, my child. Our paths are now linked throughout all of time by the power of our love for Krishna, which resides in this *murti*. Hold it to your heart and listen for the Call of the Flute whenever you are in need." He sees the life that is ahead of her, remaining silent in the mystery of what has not yet come to pass. For it is a life of persecution and hardship as in his dream, but also of great joy and devotion, for the Blue God will be her guiding light and consolation.

6. <u>Eternal Vows</u>

Sister, the Lord of the Poor

Came to wed me in a dream.

Fifty-six crores of deities formed the bridal procession

And the bridegroom was the Lord of Braj.

In my dream

I saw the wedding-arch constructed

And the Lord took my hand.

In my dream,

I underwent a wedding-ceremony

And entered the married state.

Giridhara has revealed Himself to Mira:

Her fortunes stem

From good deeds in past birth.

(#27 Alston 44-5)

A few years later, Mira is standing on the balcony of the fortress palace of Merta with her mother. Suddenly she hears the sound of pounding hooves and the music of trumpets accompanied by the raucous beating of drums, coming closer in a colorful procession. She sees a garlanded man with an ornately jeweled turban approaching on a white horse all decked in fine fabrics and tinkling bells. His festive male relatives accompany him, singing and dancing with exuberance. Mira asks what all this excitement is about.

Her mother tells her that it is a wedding procession and the groom is coming with his relations to the house of his bride.

Mira wants to know who her bridegroom will be. Of course her mother does not know. But Mira pesters her over and over until finally, in exasperation, the Rani says that the Lord Krishna will be her bridegroom, playfully pointing to the *murti* that accompanies the young princess wherever she goes. To silence her daughter's incessant pleas, the mother acts out a marriage ceremony for Mira and the little statue, not realizing that she is giving sanction and literally betrothing her daughter to the Dark One.

The Queen creates a make believe miniature *mandap*, the traditional bridal pavilion, out of peacock feathers, hanging beads, and sheer fabric. She decorates Mira with jewels fit for a bride from her own wedding trousseau. She tells her daughter that the eyes on the peacock feathers will serve as witness to the rites. They pretend that the eyes belong to all the many gods and goddesses who are attending as guests to bless this auspicious event.

Next the Queen washes Mira's feet and also bathes the *murti* to purify them both, then lights the sacred fire using a cauldron from the kitchen for the container. To make the play more realistic, she leads her daughter in the call and response of the *Saptapadi*, the seven steps of commitment all couples take in the orthodox Hindu marriage ritual. Mother and daughter echo the traditional vows and promises back and forth as Mira steps along the path leading to the joining of man and woman. Holding her little Krishna close to her heart in an embrace, it seems as though she is walking with a handsome, living, breathing man instead of the *murti*. .As the final part of the ceremony, the Rani places the amulet of the Dark-skinned Flute Player around Mira's neck to take the place of the *Mangalsutra*, the traditional marriage necklace, and showers her with fragrant rose petals.

As the ceremony progresses, the giggling of the two participants diminishes until complete silence prevails. The intent becomes more and more serious. It no longer has the quality of a game of make believe between mother and daughter. In Mira's imagination, the *murti* has taken on a life of its own and is alive with the enchanting personality of her beloved Krishna. She can hear the faint melody of a flute coming from a great distance. Then it increases in volume until it seems to be arising directly from the little statue of Krishna. When she questions her mother about the heavenly music, the Rani laughs, saying it must be the Dark One answering their call. For she too hears the song of the Flute and remembers her meeting with Krishna under the Wish Fulfilling Tree in Braj.

Influenced deeply by her mother's actions, from this time on Mira considers herself to be the wife of Krishna. In her heart, she has made a sacred, eternal vow that can never be broken. And as all Rajasthani women are, she is entirely devoted in the selfless service of *seva* to her husband/god. The family encourages Mira's religious fervor, for they too are part of the new mood of devotion through love called *bhakti* that is sweeping the land.

7. Lalita *Sakhi*

Sometime later, Mira is given a handmaiden named Lalita, a common practice for a royal maiden approaching womanhood. The princess is growing into a lovely young woman and it is time for her to have a teacher and a guide to the feminine arts. Unknown to the family, Lalita is a *gopi* from a former life, the handmaiden to Radha, Beloved of Krishna. In this lifetime, she will be Mira's companion throughout the rest of her life, the handmaiden once again to the Beloved of Krishna. Lalita is to be a *sakhi* or confidante to the young princess and will be thought of as a friend rather than as a servant. From the first moment, she understands the role she will play as their life together unfolds. Over time, Mira too recognizes the extraordinary nature of their connection.

It is Lalita's influence that allows Mira to come fully to *bhakti* rather than to the scholarly Brahmin scriptures she has been exposed to. Lalita knows how to experience the play of life, like a breath of fresh air amidst the many stern males of this warrior family. She is also expert at playing the veena, the musical instrument of Goddess Saravati.

One night, Mira is unable to sleep and so she slips away to the tiny, secluded family *mandir* in the palace gardens. As Mira approaches the little temple, she sees the very faint glow of a lit candle. And she begins to hear the soft chanting of a *mantra* to the Blue God. Watching through the veiled portal to the innermost shrine, Mira can see Lalita bent down drawing a large *yantra* with colored chalks on the floor. The complex geometric pattern takes shape as Lalita painstakingly creates a *mandala* with intricate strokes. Time passes as she chants a *mantra* to invoke the Blue God all the while forming the magic circle. At the center, within the combination of squares and triangles, a peacock feather with a prominent eye is drawn as the focus. This is the *bindhu* or source of all creation. Lalita has created an entire universe in miniature.

Now, instead of calling down the deity to enter the *yantra* as is normally done, Lalita steps into the center herself. Closing her eyes, she stands tall and lithe as the Tree of Life with her arms outstretched like branches and begins to move through a series of hand *mudras* and gestures. She begins with her palms held together at her breast pointing upwards as a sign of receptiveness. She brings them to her forehead in greeting, then stretches her hands out to welcomes the deity, and finally lays them again at her breast in submission. Raising her hands in adoration and worship, she salutes the divine Blue God.

And then, little by little, Lalita takes on the blue hue of the Lord.

Shining with energy. she is no longer Mira's familiar *sakhi*, but appears now as an androgynous figure. And she is garlanded with tulasi, has a peacock feather in her hair, and holds a flute. Mira sees the blueness of Krishna's essence enter her *sakhi,* and can no longer distinguish reality from illusion. The two faces waver between feminine and masculine, back and forth and finally blend and merge. Lalita and Krishna become one and the same.

The Divine One begins to play His flute, calling the devotee to the rites. Mesmerized by the lyrical melody, Mira is propelled into the temple and falls to the floor, prostrating herself in awe. As she arises, Krishna smiles lovingly at Mira but cautions her with a raised hand that she cannot enter the *bindhu* unprepared. Instead His love for her reaches across this barrier and Mira is engulfed in feelings of oneness with the divine. And He tells her that she will come to Him in the future for all of time. Thus, she receives the blessing of the Dark One before His form fades and Lalita returns in her ordinary form to embrace her. No words are ever spoken about the shared experience. But for both maiden and *sakhi*, there exists an implicit understanding of what has transpired between them and they know that their connection will never be broken in this life or any other.

Over time, Mira is educated by Lalita in art, dance, literature, and music. Great talent shines through her melodious voice and she begins to compose devotional *padas* to Krishna. Many nights she dreams of singing and dancing to the sublime melody of a flute within the confines of a magic circle of music and love. And when the morning comes, she makes the musical memories into beautiful harmonies of divine inspiration. Mira has found her Muse in Krishna.

8. <u>Without Krishna, There is No Song</u>

Oh friend, I sit alone while the world sleeps.

In the palace that held love's pleasure

The abandoned one sits.

She who once threaded a necklace of pearls is now stringing tears.

He has left me. The night passes while I count stars.

When will the Hour arrive?

This sorrow must end. Mira says: Lifter of Mountains, return.

(Bly/Hirshfield 24)   Trans. Hirshfield

As Mira grows to young womanhood the peaceful life of the palace begins to change. When her mother dies suddenly, she is left to the care of the men of the family. But the Rajasthanis, who are known for their heroism and valor, are fighting the Moghuls. Her father is often away in battle and Mira is alone much of the time. The loss of her mother is devastating and she grieves deeply for many months. It is only with the care and comfort of Lalita and the passage of time that the pain begins to soften though it will always be with her. Mira's heart has been broken wide open through love once again.

The time comes when, for political reasons, the House of Rathore must make an alliance with another more powerful Rajasthani family, the House of Sisodiya in Chittor, the City of Valor. Mira is to be married sight unseen to Bhoj Raj, the heir to the throne. This is all decided despite Mira's insistent and anguished pleas that she is already married to Krishna. The only words that bring solace to the princess are the names of her beloved Blue God. None but Lalita can see into the darkness of despair in her heart. As the arrangements progress from a distance, Mira becomes more and more distraught. But she has been trained in the Rajput tradition of sacrifice and womanly duty, and she knows she cannot refuse this alliance.

In Lalita's mind, an urgent plan forms, for she must do her part to help her Lady Mira. She knows that an act of magic and great faith is required. Over the miles, Lalita summons Raidas, the *guru*, the untouchable. She calls and calls to him sensing in her heart that he has heard her plea. Together they will do a great *puja* to marry Mira to Krishna, so that He will be her eternal protector and benefactor, her Sacred Husband. Over this great distance, Raidas cannot possibly arrive in time. But the Lord Krishna sees all and provides His sacred cow Surabhi as a vehicle of swift transportation. In the blink of an eye, Raidas is astonished to find himself standing within the walled gardens of the House of Rathore.

And so, for the forty- one days of established tradition, Mira is prepared by Lalita and Raidas. She prays incessantly to be given Krishna as a husband and the amulet from her Mother never leaves her neck. Day after day Mira meditates and makes offerings of flowers, fruit, incense, honey, milk. She sings the *padas* she has composed to honor her Lord and dances before His image in the temple. Mira's mind has become still like a calm pool of water, open and receptive to what must be done. Her voice has been enhanced in fullness and beauty by her endless praise and song. And she has danced herself into a state of divine ecstasy, leaving her body to become one with Krishna.

9. <u>The Sacred Marriage</u>

It is the night of the full moon in the month of Shravana, the time of the Rasa Lila. On the morrow, Bhoj Raj the groom from Chittor, will arrive for his arranged wedding to Mira. A huge canopied tent has been erected in the courtyard and adorned with strings of pearls and precious gems, sheer exotic fabrics, and strands of tiny tinkling bells to enclose the ceremony. The *kunda* or container for the fire that will serve as the focus of the ceremony has been prepared with prayer and blessings. The bride's henna, signifying the strength of love in marriage, has been applied in the Mendhi Ceremony and all is ready for the wedding rites.

Now the full moon has risen and all is quiet in the House of Rathore. Silently, secretly, Lalita and Raidas come to Mira's chambers, whispering, "the time is now, now." Without further words, they garb her in the red *saari* of the bride and decorate her with golden jewels. Mira is resplendent with ornaments, lavishly outfitted as befits a royal princess. The part of her hair is decorated with the traditional string of pearls that all brides wear. An already stunning young maiden is transformed into a goddess.

Soundlessly they make their way to the courtyard and stand under the decorative arch woven of tulasi, to watch for the arrival of the Groom. As if by magic, not a soul stirs in the palace. It is as though the companions are moving under a veil of protection, a cloak of invisibility which none can penetrate. The Goddess Maya has arrived to weave Her magic spell of illusion.

Softly they begin the Hare Krishna chant. It goes on and on endlessly. Slowly the three companions sink into a state of blissful trance. They have entered the place between the worlds where all things are possible. As if from some far away enchanted land, the sound of a flute can be heard. It beckons them even deeper into this place between the worlds. As the three friends chant, Lalita and Raidas work together to draw the sacred *yantra* to call the Blue God into their midst.   Within the bridal pavilion, a center of power is created through the making of this design that will keep the worshippers safe from intruding influences and provide an entrance to paradise.

Now a festive procession is drawing near and the Groom approaches riding regally astride the ornately decorated Sacred Cow Surabhi. This is the *barat* of the Lord and a beautiful blue skinned man arrives surrounded by His divine companions and devotees amidst a blaze of singing, joyously ringing bells, and dancing. He dismounts and strides right into the center of the *yantra*, standing on the *bindhu*, the source and center of the universe as the palace sleeps on.

The Groom is more beautiful than the full moon itself. He is garlanded in a myriad of blossoms, befitting His royal status. And His
wedding turban sports a peacock feather indicating who this Groom
is. His smile is so radiant it can melt the heart of an unbeliever.
The three companions are utterly enchanted and drawn into the
spell of His divine being.

With the first glimpse, Mira is entranced and ecstatic with love for
her Groom. His beauty and charisma have already won her devotion forever. The endless longing and waiting is about to be fulfilled. And she remembers her childhood dream: "The Dark One
was groom in my dream. I saw the festal arch, I felt a husband's
touch, I stepped into the married state."

A hushed moment of silence settles upon the scene as Raidas and
Lalita bring a veiled Mira into the center of the *yantra*. When the
cloth is removed, the bride and groom look into each other's eyes
for the first time. The Blue God knows Mira immediately as His
beloved eternal consort Radha. Raidas and Lalita enact the *Kanya
Dan* or Entrusting of the Daughter giving the Groom Mira's hand so
all is in readiness for this sacred union, the Rasa Lila of Love. Then
Raidas, who is acting as *pandit* for the ceremony, puts the *Vara-*

mala or sacred rope around their necks to signify the tying of the eternal knot of connection. This is no dream, but the reality beyond the Veil of Maya.

Now the couple is making the offerings to the sacred fire. Mira places her cupped hands in His and together they pour rice grains into the fire. The flames blaze up in acceptance of this gift of love. Mira is asked to step with her right foot upon a large stone showing that she is willing to face the challenges of conjugal life as a devoted wife. The ritual continues as Mira and her groom walk around the fire leading one another as Raidas intones the blessings. At each time around, they stop and touch their toes to the stone in their path knowing that together they can overcome any obstacles in their life.

And now the final sacred act is about to be performed, the *Sapta-padi* or Ritual of the Seven Steps. Raidas asks them to concentrate upon seven vows as they take seven steps toward each other. This stepping together signifies the shared journey the couple will take, joining them together for all of eternity. Krishna blesses the marriage necklace, the amulet of the Dark-Skinned Flute Player given to Mira by her mother years ago which now will serve as the *Mangalsutra*, signifying her married state. At the end, the Groom recites the traditional wedding *mantra*: 'I am the words and you are the melody. I am the melody and you are the words.' The words flow forth in song as Mira sings them back accompanied by Murali, the flute of infinite joy.

10. <u>Consummation</u>

Come to my pavilion, O my King.

I have spread a bed,

Made of delicately selected buds and blossoms,

And have arrayed myself in bridal garb

From head to toe.

I have been Thy slave during many births,

Thou art the be-all of my existence.

Mira's Lord is Hari, the Indestructible.

Come, grant me Thy sight at once.

(#151 Alston 96)

Attendants mysteriously appear and hoist the bridal pair onto an exquisitely painted open *doli* made in the form of a peacock. The artistry is so perfect that the bird looks alive, making it appear as though the bride and groom are suspended in the air riding on the back of a majestic bird. The newly sanctified couple is ritually escorted, silently, solemnly, out of the courtyard, through the palace, to Mira's chambers. Not a soul stirs for the companions are protected and secluded in another time and place, far beyond the Veil of Maya.

In the royal apartments, the couple is seated upon a wooden bed that is carved with floral motifs, richly garbed and curtained. They are showered with the petals of sweet smelling flowers while in-cense and candles are lit giving the room a soft glow. A circle of protection is created by Raidas and Lalita so none may intrude upon this intimate moment. And then, the two are left alone under the spell of this *puja* of the full moon to consummate that which has been made sacred. This is Mira's initiation into the Arts of Love, the becoming of One with the Beloved.

As Krishna gently removes Mira's bridal veil and looks upon her face as His consecrated bride, the Veil of Maya that separates reality and illusion is lifted in the universe. Her radiant and ethereal beauty reminds Him of His beloved eternal consort Radha and he knows Mira to be one and the same in another life and personality. Through His divinity, Krishna takes on His multitude of forms in the guise of the elements of nature. Mirabai reflects back each and every mood and image, mirroring His divinity.

And so they begin as two separate gusts of wind. They brush against each other tentatively and then with more purpose. Soon they are weaving in and out of each other's auras in the magical Dance of Creation. The rhythm of their separate breaths creates a counterpoint of sound, a duet of the masculine and feminine. Join-ing together, they become the One Breath of Life in a symphony of vast, celestial harmony. Their spirits are soaring and winging off into the outer realms; they are floating between the worlds. At last, they become a pair of cooing doves returning to the nest, as the peace and stillness of twilight descends upon them.

And then they are two separate flames of candlelight, mere sparks of what they could become together. They dip in and out of each other's light, feeding upon each other, creating a single light that grows with exaltation into a roaring bonfire. The flames erupt into molten lava, exploding through their *chakras*. *Kundalini* energy is vibrating as Mira becomes the Flame of Creation. She is transformed and transmuted in the Alchemy of Love. Afterwards, they bask together in the afterglow of the glorious sunset of their love.

Now they are two glistening droplets of water held in the monsoon clouds. Mother Nature releases them in a gentle rain and they fall together into a still pool of water, floating together in bliss. Cradled there in perfect love and perfect trust, they begin to move, slowly at first, gaining momentum, until they tumble joyously through a sparkling waterfall into the River of Life. Here they are drawn in an ever-increasing charge of energy and motion, moving inexorably to the sea. As they enter the ocean upon the crashing waves, they are mingled with all that is, churned, transformed, and birthed into the flux and flow of the Great Waters. The lovers transform into a pair of swans gliding with grace upon the now still waters, mated for life.

Upon the fallow earth, the purple clouds of the monsoon part to shed tears of joy from the eyes of Heaven. Like tiny gleaming pearls, the drops of moisture fall upon the parched soil to refresh the body of the Living Earth greening the land. Krishna takes on the guise of the Great Father Sky. He shines His radiant light, the Sun, down upon Mira who is the Great Earth Mother. His winds exhale the Breath of Creation upon Her body. Their heartbeats, like the pulse of Mother Earth's drum beat, are synchronized in perfect tempo. Soon there is an awakening coming from the depths of the earth, a quickening, as the seed germinates and begins to send up a tendril, ever seeking the light of God. The seedling erupts through the soil and soaks in the energy of the Dark Lord. The rains, the sun, the winds nourish it, until it peaks into an exquisite, exotic bloom of rare beauty and fragrance.

When the new day dawns, Mira is alone in her bed. But the marriage that has happened under the full moon of Shavrana has transformed her and will always remain in her heart. Through the consummate touch of Her Lord Krishna, Mira is the eternal virgin, a maiden unto herself, returning once more to what she was. The Blue God has given her faith in the future and a promise that all will be well as she moves along this new path into her arranged marriage. He tells her to be like the *gopis* in the time of the *Rasa Lila,* who cared for their husbands and families even while being total-ly devoted to Him. And at the last, before departing, Krishna has shown Himself as her future groom with a different face and tells Mira she will recognize Him again in the form of another just as she will remember Him in every form of nature.

11. Arjuna

At the same moment under the full moon in Shravana, Bhoj Raj, the handsome young prince of Chittor, heir apparent, courageous warrior of the Sisodiya clan, has a remarkable dream vision as well. At his personal shrine, he sits in lotus pose and offers his soul to the Divine. Deep in prayer on the eve before his marriage, he enters a trance state and has a visitation.

Behind his third eye, Bhoj Raj senses the presence of an entity that encompasses all things. He hears the hypnotic and lyrical song of Murali, the Divine Flute, and the image of the blue skinned God crowned with peacock feathers begins to form. Though he has always venerated Durga as the family deity, there is an instant recognition and sense of kinship between the prince and the Dark Lord. Krishna's wondrously sweet smile radiates out waves of love and deep affection towards the prince. Greeting him as Arjuna, He opens his mouth to show him another life.

Wondering why he is being called Arjuna, Bhoj Raj realizes with astonishment that he is part of the epic *Mahabharata* and that his name in this past incarnation is Arjuna of the Pandava tribe. Krishna knows that the personality of Arjuna is tender hearted and in need of strengthening. And so He says, "I am going to give you yourself

Arjuna." He tells the prince to go out into the grove nearby and pick the fruit of the sacred Arjuna Tree as an offering to Him.

Bhoj Raj follows the Blue God's instructions. In obeisance, he bows at the feet of the Lord. Krishna breathes upon the offering, passes His hand over it in blessing and it becomes *prasad*. As the prince eats the sanctified fruit, he feels himself becoming more and more of Arjuna and less of Bhoj Raj. And Arjuna becomes all of who he really is, a noble warrior prince. He remembers and feels now the mutual love he shares with Krishna. This bond is the light of the world for both men, more valuable and cherished than any riches, power, or fame in life.

Suddenly Bhoj Raj is alone on a battlefield in his previous life as Arjuna. He knows he must fight a war with his own kin for the throne, to determine who has the right to rule. Looking over the battlefield, he contemplates what will befall him and is filled with dread. Plagued with abject terror, he throws down his bow in despair. It is the dark night of the soul, the valley of sorrows, a spiritual abyss that feels hopeless and bottomless to Arjuna. He stands now upon the battleground of Kurukshetra.

Arjuna turns to the heavens and begs for help. And so, the Blue God descends in His Golden Chariot and comes to him in his time of need. Although he does not yet know it, Arjuna has given over the reins of his life into the hands of his dearly beloved friend, who is the Divine Charioteer, Lord Krishna in disguise. Stretching out His palms to Arjuna in welcome and friendship, Krishna reminds him that he was born into the *caste* of rulers and warriors, and is a defender of justice.

To fight this battle is Arjuna's *dharma*, his destiny. As a prince of the *Ksatriya* or warrior caste, he must act according to his own nature and cannot do otherwise to fulfill his purpose in this vast drama of life and death. This is a righteous war, waged for the most esteemed values of liberty and truth. Arjuna is told in firm and un-wavering language that he must do his required service in the world and fight this battle with joy and confidence. For the outcome either way will bring him the peace of heaven or the victory of an earthly kingdom.

Krishna then speaks about the eternal and the transitory in the world. To illustrate His teachings, Arjuna is instructed to take a seat in the back of the Golden Chariot while Krishna handles the reins. Urging the shining white horses on, the chariot rises into the air, light and swift as a flying carpet. Soon Krishna and Arjuna are float-ing high above the battlefield with a panoramic view of the entire scene. From this vantage point, Arjuna is shown an over view of the meaning of life.

The Blue God tells Arjuna to look through his third eye to see beyond normal sight all that is unfolding on the battlefield in preparation for war. Trusting his friend, the prince sees what the Lord sees- not the mortal forms of his relations but the pure light bodies of their immortal souls, dancing in the never ending Cycle of birth, life, death, and rebirth. Though their faces, genders, and forms differ, the spirit within continues on without change for all of eternity. Opening his eyes, Arjuna again sees only the material world. except now the Blue God has given him a deeper vision into the other realm and the understanding that death is an illusion and the soul is eternal.

12. *Vishwarupa,* The One Who Shows the Universal Form

Arjuna now knows Krishna to be his *guru,* but His divinity is yet hidden. His fear still grips him as he sees the impending catastrophe of destruction. He begs the Blue God to show him more reason to fight. Thus Krishna reveals His true identity and shows Arjuna the vast multiplicity yet Oneness that God is. The Lord becomes Vishwarupa, the One who shows the Universal Form.

And so, the Divine Eye is given to Arjuna and he is enabled to see Krishna in his glorious and majestic form as God. His eyes are anointed with the Pure Nectar of Love, and he is allowed a glimpse into the incomprehensible and unknowable mystery of the Lord. Arjuna's vision is magnified and sensitized beyond what his mind has ever conceived possible. This revelation is like the light of a thousand suns and moons in the sky amidst a glittering canopy of jewel-like stars, the invaluable gems of spiritual vision. The cells and atoms of all things dance in joyous freedom in this wondrous vision.

Suddenly the battlefield of Kurukshetra vanishes. There is no sight or sound below, only complete silence and stillness. An eerie glow lights up the heavens and the ground trembles. And then, Time stands still as Krishna begins to change, transform, metamorphose, shedding His *maya* and coming forth as the God that He is. Arjuna hears without sound a voice as deep as thunder, and yet as soft and gentle as the whisper of angels. He sees without sight a vision of a radiant rainbow of colors he has never imagined possible. And he feels without touch an all- encompassing embrace, enfolding him like a child in the arms of a loving parent, giving him sanctuary in eternal, unconditional love.

As Arjuna looks upon Krishna in His cosmic form, he sees all the worlds and times that have ever been, all the Gods and Goddesses worshipped by all people, all the seasons and landscapes of the earth, the vast panorama of the entire universe. He feels the bliss of joy and laughter, knows generosity and compassion, desires abundance and prosperity for all of humanity. He is moved by the ultimate beauty and peace of the soul as mirrored in the elements of nature, receiving the essence of *prema* or Divine Love. Krishna is Vishwatma, He Who is the Soul of the Universe.

But now, filled with horrific power, Krishna manifests in His terrible form as the Lord of Destruction and Annihilation before Arjuna's startled eyes. A wailing wind sweeps over the land. Ugly, black birds of prey, the raven and the vulture, circle overhead searching for their victims. Vicious predator beasts, the hyena and the jackal,

115

stalk the field straining with hunger to kill and devour their helpless prey. The skies are a black void of death as if the world was coming to an end. The sun is eclipsed, the moon is covered in darkness, and even the stars are completely obliterated by a thick veil of storm-filled clouds.

Krishna becomes Kala, All-consuming Time, the inevitable and merciless demise of all living things. He becomes the howling whirlwind that blows away all that is no longer needed, the raging flood that washes away all that is not pure, and the uncontrollable forest fire that burns away everything in its path. He is the earthquake that shatters our very foundations and splits the earth in half, the inescapable, tumultuous vortex that destroys the universe, shattering it into a million tiny, irreparable pieces. He is the scorching heat of the desert that withers and desiccates all traces of living humanity and the freezing ice of an arctic winter storm that is so cold it takes the breath away and freezes the blood. The Apocalypse has come.

Like a flash of lightning, the Dark God shatters our illusions and all that we hold dear to make way for necessary change and spiritual enlightenment. Krishna is the paradox of opposites as He shapeshifts in and out of these many qualities with such rapidity and fluency that everything begins to blend together into a blur before Arjuna's overwhelmed eyes. Pleading with Krishna to return again to

His beautiful and loving form as the Blue God, Arjuna understands that He is the unborn, undying essence of all life. In Him, all that was lost is found; all that was hidden is seen, all that was unknown is known, all that was broken is healed and made whole again.

.

Returning to His benevolent form once again, the Blue God smiles serenely with trust in His devotee and gives him the freedom to choose his own fate.

> Thus I have explained to you
> the most confidential of all knowledge
> Deliberate on this fully,
> and then do what you wish to do.
> Lord Krishna *Bhagavad Gita* 18.63 (Prabhupada 704)

Uplifted and filled with awe, Arjuna decides that he will fight for his *karmic* destiny. The Lord sounds His cosmic conch shell to start the battle. Arjuna joins in on his conch and together they make a primal sound that vibrates and circulates all over the universe. The deep, booming vibration, like the roaring of an angry lion or a fierce demon, clears away all negativity. The sound waves, that are more noise than melody to human ears, create an oscillating wind of such strength and proportion that it blows away all possibility of defeat. And so it is that the *Bhagavad Gita*, the Celestial Song of the Exalted One, is given as a gift from Lord Krishna to all of humanity.

13. <u>Surrogate Husband</u>

The dream vision of Kurukshetra returns to the present. Bhoj Raj knows now that he has always belonged to the Lord Krishna. He remembers the deep love and companionship he shared with the Dark One in his life as Arjuna. The loyalty and brotherhood between them extends beyond time and place and he will do whatever is required for his dearly beloved friend in any incarnation.

Merging now with Mira's trance experience of the Sacred Marriage that is taking place simultaneously, Bhoj Raj sees the bridal pavilion at the House of Rathore made beautiful with garlands and palms. He sees the Altar of Pearl Tears that has been decorated with sacred markings. He sees the cauldron for the fire that will serve as the focus of his marriage ceremony the next day. And he sees a beautiful veiled bride, without knowing her identity, surrounded by her companions awaiting her bridegroom.

A lyrical yet commanding flute sounds in the distance announcing the approach of the *barat*. And now Bhoj Raj sees the entire ceremony of the Sacred Marriage taking place before his amazed eyes. He sees that the groom is his Lord Krishna in His aspect as *Keshava*, The One with the Beautiful Long Hair. And it appears that the radiant bride is Radha, the Consort of His Master, *Guru*, and Lord.

Weeping, his heart expands and opens as Bhoj Raj becomes aware of the profound sacredness of what he is being honored to see and experience. Although he has never seen her face before, when the veil is lifted from her face he understands that his betrothed Mira and Radha are one and the same. Krishna looks directly at him and without uttering a single word, lays with trust the responsibility upon His devotee to care for and protect Mira. For Bhoj Raj and Mira will marry the next day as arranged. It is part of their destiny, but they must enact it according to the design of the Lord. Bhoj Raj understands that he must fulfill his sacred duty to Krishna once again. He consents willingly with all of his heart and soul, for there is nothing the prince would not do for the Blue God. He knows now that Mira is not really of this world and will never belong to him in a traditional marriage.

The following day, the morning of the wedding dawns bright and clear and all proceeds as has been ordained. The buoyancy and energy of the *barat* gives Bhoj Raj the courage and the fortitude to proceed for there is still a vague sense of apprehension within the groom who has not yet fully understood the impact of the message of his dream vision. Although he has seen her face in the vision of the Sacred Marriage, he has not met Mira before and must wait until her marriage veil is lifted to be sure of what he has experienced.

And so it is that Bhoj Raj arrives at the House of Rathore on his regal white stallion decked as a groom. When he hears the sound of the sacred conch shell being blown to announce his entrance, he remembers how Krishna blew His conch to start the war at Kurukshetra. He knows then that the Lord is again present here and now with him.

Bhoj Raj is garlanded and decorated with the sacred signs and brought to the *mandap.* A sheet separates him from his betrothed and the ceremony proceeds. When the veil is lifted, the melody of the Mystic Flute *Murali* begins to sing of love and devotion to the couple. None of the audience in attendance thinks to question where the heavenly music comes from, knowing only in their subconscious minds that something supernatural is happening.

As the bride and groom look into each other's eyes for the first time, there is an immediate recognition followed by relief. Mira looks exactly like the Bride and Consort of Krishna as seen in the prince's mystical vision. And Bhoj Raj has the face of the Other shown to her by Krishna after the Sacred Marriage *puja.* Delighted laughter bubbles under the surface of their minds as they nod in recognition of each other as fellow devotees. Their destiny together becomes clear. The common nerves and worries that have plagued the couple evaporate as a force bigger than both of them envelopes them in complete harmony.

As the *Varamala*, the Sacred Rope, is tied around their necks, it begins to glow with a blue mist that is the essence of Krishna's divine energy. They continue through the ceremony knowing in their hearts and souls that they are offering themselves to Manamohan, the Enchanter of Hearts. As they circle the marriage fire, the old *murti* from Mira's childhood sits upon the altar, taking on the reality of flesh for their eyes, acting as Sacred Witness.

One of the guests at the wedding is a Gypsy Crone from the desert. As the ceremony concludes, the time comes for the *Mangalsutra* to be given to the bride. The Ancient One steps forth and asks Mira for her old amulet of the dark skinned flute player so it can be exchanged for the traditional jewel of commitment. When Mira hesitates, she hears Krishna's flute singing a melody in her mind, telling her the talisman must now be returned to the Keeper. For in the fullness of time, all things return and she will wear it once more with even deeper meaning.

14. <u>Fortress Walls</u>

I was standing at the door of my house

When Mohan passed.

He was smiling gently.

His face radiant as the moon.

My relatives reproach me and crack bitter jests,

But my wayward eyes brook no obstruction.

They are sold and belong to another.

Whether they praise or chide me,

I accept whatever is said

And raise it reverently to my forehead.

Says Mira: Without my Master, Giridhara,

I cannot exist for a second.

(#13 Alston 38)

When the feasting and celebration have ended, the time comes for the couple to leave for the groom's ancestral home. The departure of the bride is traditionally a time of emotion and tears, of joy and sorrow, of leave takings and new beginnings. The sound of crying fills the air at the leaving of the daughter, Mira. Bhoj Raj gently takes her hand leading her to the *doli*, the ceremonial decorative cart that will carry Mira to her new home.

As Mira is lifted onto the *doli* she is showered with flower petals and rice for good luck. Her handmaiden Lalita, who will accompany her to her new home, walks by her side. As Raidas whispers in her ear, Mira recalls hearing this same message as a young girl: "Remember me as I will remember you, for we will meet again, my Child." And silently, unobtrusively, the *guru* melts into the crowd of well-wishers. Bhoj Raj mounts his stallion leading the *doli* with majesty and authority to the Sisodiya palace.

As they travel through the countryside, well-wishers line the way. The crowd is jubilant and excited to see the handsome couple destined to become their rulers. Cheering and singing accompany the procession as it makes its way toward Chittor. Bhoj Raj waves gallantly to the assembly but Mira is suddenly shy and retreats behind the curtains of the *doli*.

Soon they come to the town of Chittor and Mira can see the fearsome and imposing stone fortress complex high above on a hill in the distance. The Fort at Chittor is the largest in all of India. Legend traces it back to the Pandavas of the *Mahaharata*. The crenelated walls appear to be hewn right into the rock as if growing from it. This symbol of Rajput valiancy looks as though no enemy could breach the mighty walls and no prisoner could ever escape, for it is completely surrounded by this thick protective enclosure.

The horse and *doli* proceed up a steep serpentine road, zigzagging through a series of seven monumental gates at different levels that straddle the path. Many gruesome iron spikes decorate each gate to warn and forbid any enemy who tries to enter. Watch towers guard each entrance. To Mira's gentle nature, the fortress gives no feeling of warmth or welcome. At many of the gates there is a temple associated with the god who names the entrance, Hanuman, Ganesha, Rama, but none to her Lord Krishna.

Beyond the fortified gates is the main entrance to the grounds. Inside, an imposing tower has been built to watch over the complex. When it is pointed out to Mira she suddenly becomes cold and frightened as though some portent is being shown to her. But the procession moves quickly forward and Mira calms the feelings of danger thinking she is only nervous about what lies ahead.

Finally they arrive at the massive courtyard entrance to the royal Palace. Family members are present to greet and welcome the newly- wed couple. The Rani, Step Mother of Bhoj Raj, receives the couple with the formal and traditional honors. Mira in turn touches the feet of the Queen Mother with respect.

After the long series of ceremonial greetings, the mood relaxes as the bride and groom play the game called *Kangana Khelna*. A ring is thrown into a dish of milk and honey and whoever finds it first will have the upper hand in the marriage. The air is filled with lighthearted laughter and jesting. Mira notices a sullen young man in the gathering who does not join in the festivities. This is Vikram, her husband's younger half-brother, second in line for the throne. Even when Mira smiles directly at him and tries to include him, he turns away, remaining apart and observing silently with a look of jealous malice on his face. When the bride and groom both grasp the ring at the same moment, it bounces out of their hands and lands right in front of Mira's *murti* of the Blue God. Suddenly, not a sound can be heard for no one present knows the meaning of this portent. But the game is finished and cannot be repeated.

After these formalities and games are over, the Rani of Chittor becomes serious, requesting that Mira worship the family deity Durga at the altar. This duty is expected of a new daughter in law without question. In doing so, she obtains blessings for her husband. If anything goes amiss, it bodes ill for the marriage and for her husband's health and future. But Mira is resolute and unyielding in her refusal to worship any other god than her beloved Krishna. A furious scene unfolds, voices are raised and angry accusations are hurled at Mira. She continues to remain calm and firm within herself and will not be coerced.

The Rani is deeply insulted and wants to be rid of Mira immediately. To her conservative and orthodox mind, this refusal is unthinkable and inauspicious. Vikram smirks with pleasure as though hoping for a conflict. And so, with her first step into Chittor, the stage is set for the challenge and later persecution of Mira. Already the fortress walls are closing in around her. But Bhoj Raj lovingly jokes with his mother, reminding her to be tolerant and gentle with his innocent young bride. The intense crisis of stalemated conflict is lifted, but only for the moment, for the Rani is not placated.

15. <u>Where White Swans Take Their Joy</u>

Friend, this body is a great ocean,

Concealing reefs and sea-vaults heaped up with jewels.

Enter its secret rooms and light your own lamp.

Within the body are gardens, rare orchids, peacocks,

the inner music.

Within the body a lake,

in its cool waters, white swans take their joy.

And in the body, a vast market-

Go there and trade, sell yourself for a profit you can't spend.

Mira says, her Lord's beauty cannot be measured.

She wants only to live near his feet.

(Bly/Hirshfield 58) Trans Hirshfield

The couple is ferried to the Lake Palace of Udaipur to spend the wedding night. For this auspicious occasion, a specially designed boat like a gondola has been created. It is in the shape of two mated swans painted in opalescent white with exquisite detail and artistry. Protected by a canopy, the sides of the little craft are curtained with beads of shimmering pearls to shelter the royal pair. For their comfort, tasseled and embroidered pillows line the bottom of the boat, so they can recline together.

The lake is placid and smooth as glass, as they glide languidly to their destination. On an island in a shimmering lake, the palace appears to float on the waters. A vision in white, it is a breath of fresh air amidst the fortress complex of Chittor, a contrast to the Rajasthani desert with its dull, monochromatic coloring.

The silent Ferrier has a magical presence that shifts and changes from moment to moment. Sometimes his face appears as a kindly old ferryman and in the next moment a laughing blue-skinned boy wearing crocodile earrings is in the stern. The similarity in persona and manner is so strong between the two that the elder could be the child's grandsire, showing how the child will look as an Old One.

The couple is brought to the bridal chamber where a canopied and veiled bed has been made beautiful with all manner of exotic fabrics. The light of the full moon filters in through the ornate *jaali* screens creating marvelous exotic patterns on the floor and walls. As they are showered with the petals of velvety, fragrant flowers, honeyed incense and a myriad of tiny candles that gleam like stars are lit for their pleasure. In the background, from far away, the soaring, irresistible melody of the flute can be heard. And then they are left alone.

Without words, Mira Bai and Bhoj Raj, in complete unity and shared intent, begin the *puja* to Lord Krishna. Chanting the *Maha Hare*

Krishna Mantra, they make offerings and prayers to the Divine One. Together they hold the *murti* to their hearts and the Call of the Flute can now be heard right in the room. The little idol begins to smile at them. A shimmering mist fills the room and the form of the Blue Skinned God comes to them speaking words of tenderness and love:

> If one offers Me with love and devotion
> A leaf, a flower, a fruit, a water
> I will accept it.
> All that you do, all that you eat,
> All that you offer and give away
> Should be done as an offering to me.
> Lord Krishna Bhagavad Gita 9.26 and 27 (Prabhupada 418-419)

In an act of endless generosity and perfect trust Krishna merges into the form of Bhoj Raj. He takes on the prince's form as the prince takes on His divine essence. Krishna/Bhoj Raj brings the flute to His lips and begins the Song of Courtship, the calling of the Beloved to the Lover. And Mira begins to sing, swaying to the melody of divine yearning. Glowing with white light, it is almost as though two graceful swans are dancing together in joy.

Soon Mira's body begins to glow and takes on a golden luminosity, as the energy of Radha, Krishna's other self, descends upon her form. The bride and groom step out of their individual personas and become the Divine Couple, wholly apart from who they are in this lifetime. Thus it is that Mirabai enters her married life in complete purity, wholly committed to her vows to Krishna. The next morning, Bhoj Raj is called to battle, leaving his new bride and never more to return.

16. <u>The Pill of Knowledge</u>

I have found a *guru* in Raidas.

He has given me the Pill of Knowledge.

I lost the honor of the royal family,

I went astray with the *sadhus*,

I constantly rise up,

Go to God's Temple and dance,

snapping my fingers.

I have thrown away the veil

I have taken refuge with the great *gurus*

And snapped my fingers at the consequences.

(Kishwar/Vanita 80)

The war with the Moguls continues to ravage the land and the royal men from both the House of Sisodiya and the House of Rathore are called to battle. There is a devastating loss of life that includes not only Mira's father and father in law but her husband Bhoj Raj. And so, Mira's life begins to change irrevocably once again.

Blaming Mira's unorthodox behavior and her love for Krishna as the cause of her husband and step son's bad luck and untimely demise, the Rani accosts her, attempting to remove the marriage vermillion and break her wedding bangles. The Rajput tradition of widowhood calls for *sati*, the self-immolation of the wife on the funeral pyre along with the body of the husband. But Mira refuses, angering the royal family further. She resists fiercely for in her heart she is married to Krishna and thus is not a widow. She will not allow anyone to erase or diminish her beloved Krishna, her immortal husband. She can never be a widow as the wife of an eternal God. Mira mourns Bhoj Raj, but she is now free to devote herself entirely to the Blue God. Her love for the Dark One is more real to her than the loss of a husband she has hardly known.

Lalita once again sends a calling to the *guru* Raidas. It is time now for him to come to Mira and continue the unfolding of her destiny. When Mira learns that Raidas has taken up residence in the town and is teaching at a temple there, she escapes from the palace in the guise of a serving woman and along with Lalita goes to meet him. The reunion is joyous and Mira embraces Raidas, publicly calling him her *guru*. His presence is like a healing elixir for Mira, medicine for her soul.

After her household duties are completed, Mira comes to meditate and worship in secret with Raidas and spends more and more time in devotion to the Dark One. Soon, other followers of Krishna hear of the goodness of the princess and begin to seek admission to her presence. With generosity and an open heart, all are welcomed here. Every day the little temple is filled to capacity and no one is ever turned away. Before long, these gatherings can no longer be kept hidden in secret.

Mira uses her fortune to care for the lower *caste* worshippers even though it is forbidden for women of royalty to mix with the poor or be looked upon by any man. As rumors begin to circulate, members of the Sisodiya family whisper and then complain loudly in anger and resentment. With the loss of both the Rana and the Heir Apparent Bhoj Raj, Vikram, the younger son of a second wife, has taken the throne. An arrogant and willful youth, he is both threatened and incensed by Mira's rebellious behavior, smugly taking note of her transgressions.

As often as she can get away, Mira disguises herself in the garb of a lower *caste* serving woman, devoid of jewels and heavily veiled. Each time she descends down the winding road from the palace to the village through the seven fortified gates that remain open during the daytime. Mira feels as though she is shedding more and more of the restrictions of the royal family as she passes each gateway. At first she is terrified of discovery, but soon her resolute heart recognizes the portals as old friends and no longer as barriers to her freedom. In her innocent and pure heart, Mira becomes fearless and carefree in her secret adventuring. But one day she begins to feel a sense of unease on her walk as if someone silent and hidden from sight is watching her.

On this day at the Temple in the town, Mira receives two visitors who have traveled far to receive her *darshan* and hear her famous *padas* to Krishna. The men seem foreign to Rajasthan but royal in bearing, despite being simply dressed and humble in manner. Lalita and Raidas bring them without question into the worship. The men sit and listen enthralled by the emotional outpouring and the soaring spirit of Mira's music. They are transported to the realms of Vrinda-vana, the eternal abode of Krishna, by the strains of the melody and devotion they hear. When at last the great power and magnetism of the *puja* is ended, they bow weeping at Mira's feet and offer her a heavy, ornate necklace of gold and precious gemstones in hom-age. At first she is reluctant to accept such a treasure, but the men reassure her that their gift is meant as an offering to the Dark One. Mira has determined that she will exchange the necklace for money to give as alms for the poor in Krishna's name.

17. <u>Poison to Nectar</u>

O my King,

Why did you bear enmity against me?

Why do you play the prickly cactus?

Now I have left the palace

And its lofty towers.

I no longer live in your city.

I have renounced antimony and tilak

And donned the ochre robe.

Mira's Lord is the courtly Giridhara;

He turned poison into nectar.

(# 34 Alston 48)

One of Vikram's spies has been secretly watching Mira for several days and following her through the gates to the temple in the village. He finds something to report on the day that the necklace is given as an offering and he takes it by force from her hands. When the prince is shown the priceless necklace, he becomes suspicious, questioning its origins. He confiscates it and plans to keep it for his own.

A rumor begins to circulate that the Mogul emperor Akbar, accompanied by his court musician Tansen, has been to the temple and heard Mira's music. It appears that these enemies have encroached upon Vikram's realm in secret and under disguise, bestowing a priceless necklace upon Mira. He is shamed and infuriated to imagine that his foes have enjoyed the company of one of his royal women who are by tradition kept in strict *purdah*, secluded and veiled, so no man may look upon them. This is a deep insult. So he locks Mira in the fortress tower, the same imposing one she noticed when arriving in Chittor.

The tower is a tall and narrow structure in complete isolation from the main palace. Mira is forced roughly up a dark and claustrophobic circular staircase. With each step, she feels more imprisoned and helpless. Finally she reaches the top and is pushed into a dank and lonely apartment with none of the royal comforts she is used to. This bleak place will be her home for life unless she changes her unorthodox ways and submits to the new Rajah. Only Lalita is allowed to attend her. Hidden under her cloak, she has managed to bring the *murti* of Krishna with her to Mira in her banishment.

One night Vikram is informed that Mira is entertaining a man in her chambers. The gossips of the palace have heard singing and sweet talk behind the locked and barricaded doors, words of devotion and love. So Vikram decides to surprise her and catch her in an illicit act. As he approaches the door to her apartment he hears murmured sounds. Rushing in with a sword in each hand, he is so

136

angry that his weapons seem to burst into flame with his rage. He finds Mira deep in trance, worshipping her *murti* of Krishna, chanting the Divine Names. As Vikram tries to attack her, Mira is multiplied into dozens of Miras appearing in every corner of the room, like the many Krishnas in the *Rasa Lila*. The Rajah runs from the room in panic and bewilderment.

Soon Vikram concocts another plan to punish and demoralize his sister-in-law. He is determined to break Mira's spirit for once and all. Ordering a servant to steal the *murti* of Krishna, Vikram shatters the statue into hundreds of tiny pieces. Then he has it thrown into the river far from the palace grounds. Mira is broken hearted when she notices that it has vanished. After her sobbing has been exhausted, she begins to move in a circular dance trying to calm her distraught emotions. Through this *puja*, she goes into the realm where she can hear Krishna calling to her with the song of His flute, calming as a lullaby. The melody carries a message that all will be well and Mira is told to go to sleep for the night and not to lose hope. The next morning, the *murti* is again on the altar beside Mira's bed, whole and unblemished. It has broken through the water and returned to its beloved untouched by the evil intentions fueled by hatred and jealousy.

When Vikram returns the next day to gloat over her unhappiness, he is shocked to find the little statue by Mira's bedside undefiled. Blinded by his ego, he cannot discern the sacred workings of the Lord Krishna behind the return of the *murti*. He sees only an inanimate idol. He tries again to deface the statue with the force of his anger but nothing can harm it. Every time he tries to grab it, the statue jumps in the air or disappears behind the prince's back as if playing a game of hide and seek. When he does manage to touch it, he has to pull away in agony as his fingers are burned raw by the spiritual heat of the God. After many frustrating attempts, Vikram feels himself paralyzed and turned to stone while the little statue stands before him, a smiling and magnificent figure radiating the vital breath of life. Mira has to hold back her laughter as the *murti* winks at her in complicity.

In his anger, the confounded Vikram tries to assassinate Mira. His cruelty is now becoming sadistic. First he sends her a cup of poison in a consecrated cup. He watches the scene as if it were a play, his stare so malignant that it nearly paralyzes Mira's will. But she takes the poison fearlessly knowing that whatever is sent to her comes from the Beloved and the consequences do not matter if it is her destiny to die. Lalita stands by with her in utter despair, trying unsuccessfully to contain her cries of fear and helplessness.

The prince watches jubilantly as his plan unfolds. But when she drinks, Mira's face and entire body blaze with health and become radiant with the energy of life. The God-intoxicated Princess laughs in delight. The poison has turned into nectar by the grace of the Blue God, for she is drinking the antidote to hatred, which is unconditional love. Nothing evil can touch Mira because she has the strength of devotion in her heart. And the sanctions of the palace and the greater society have no power here. Holding the *murti* to her heart *chakra*, the music of the flute bursts out joyously into the room, sounding like a dance of celebration. Everyone can hear it except for the prince, for he is in a state of ignorance and delusion. But even this fantastic event does not touch Vikram's heart and he continues to slander and revile Mira's name and character.

The next day, a basket is sent to Mira in the tower. It appears to be an innocent gift but it holds an ominous secret. Inside, a deadly viper has been concealed in several succulent pieces of fruit and this is given to her as an offering for Krishna. Mira lays the gift at the feet of the *murti* and when she opens the basket she finds a snake with the sacred *tulasi* garland of Krishna around its neck. The snake bows its head to her, licks her hand, and jumps to her neck encircling it like a necklace. As the snake surrounds Mira's neck, it transforms into an ornament to adorn the princess. The fruit has become *prasad* and Mira enjoys a delicious repast as a gift from the Blue God.

When this tactic fails, Vikram tries one last time to end Mira's life. His inventive cruelty has no limits and he conjures up a painful torture for her. A bed of iron stakes is brought to Mira's chambers and she is forced to lie down in it. She breathes deeply, closes her eyes, and chants a song to Krishna softly under her breath. As she reclines, each stake turns into a fragrant garland of yellow and orange marigolds, to create a bower of delight for Mira's rest.

18. <u>The Heels of the Wanderer</u>

Sister, if the king of the House of Sisodiya rages

What can he do?

I shall continue to sing the glories of Govinda

If the king becomes angry

He may keep his kingdom and be welcome.

But if Hari becomes angry

I shall lose lustre like a withering flower.

I do not observe the rules of worldly decorum.

(#35 Alston 48)

In a final act of vengeance and enmity, the defeated Vikram curses and harangues his sister in law, forcing her to leave his realm. Spewing words of hatred, he orders her to drown herself in the river outside of the fortress grounds. Lalita attends her as they leave the palace and go down to the water. Outwardly, Mira seems intent on drowning herself, but in her heart she knows Krishna will intervene for her once again. She walks calmly into the river with great dignity and bearing, singing her songs in praise of the Blue God.

The water, like the embrace of the Dark One, holds her and she cannot sink. The waves begin to surround her and in a state of ecstasy, she loses consciousness. A gentle but firm hand pulls her back from the river and the triumphant Flute Song of the Exalted

One can be heard by those who are able to hear. Strong arms lift Mira and carry her to the opposite shore, away from the palace and her old life. She is rescued and sheltered in the embrace of the Divine Blue God. Krishna tells Mira that her life as a Rajput Princess is over and she belongs wholly to Him. But now she must seek Him in Vrindavana.

Always think of Me,

become my devotee, worship Me

and offer your homage to Me.

Thus will you come to Me without fail.

I promise you this because you are My very dear friend.

Abandon all varieties of religion

and just surrender to Me.

I shall deliver you from all sinful reactions.

Do not fear.

Lord Krishna, *Bhagavad Gita* 18.65-66 (Prabhupada 591)

Accompanied only by her companion Lalita, Mira begins her journey, a pilgrimage that few dare to undertake to know the Dark One. She leaves behind all of the possessions from her former life of royalty, taking only her *veena* and the *murti* of her beloved Krishna. They will go to Vrindavana in Braj, the abode of the Blue God, seeking a gateway to communion with the divine.

Every faithful Lover of the Dark One will eventually receive a glimpse of Braj, for this Paradise is within the reach of all who truly love Him. In his dreams, Raidas sees Mira in the desert. He feels an immense empathy, for her as he has walked the Thar as well. But he remembers his very first dream vision of her in Madhuban, the Forest of Sweetness, and knows that this arduous journey and its trials will pass and she will arrive at the place of her destiny.

Mira goes to pay homage to Raidas who has returned to his secluded hut deep in the forest. She wants to receive his guidance and blessing for her journey. He speaks to her in riddles, telling her to follow the Secret Path, to go to the place where everything is music and song, seeing without sight, hearing without sound, feeling without touch. Her *guru* tells her that he will be with her in spirit throughout the long pilgrimage and they will meet again in Vrindavana. He tells Mira that when every path seems closed before her, the Divine One with the heavenly Blue Skin will open a Secret Path. She must only have faith and surrender all fears to the Beloved Lord. As she leaves him, Raidas reminds Mira of the blessing of pilgrimage with words from the *Aitareya Brahmana*, the Book of Hymns:

Flower-like are the heels of the wanderer.

Thus his body grows and is fruitful.

All his sins disappear, slain by the toil of his journeying.

(*Sama Veda* 446)

Thus it is that Mira crosses out of royal society and its constraints, seeking salvation in the form of union with the Blue God. She begins a Journey of Asceticism, as Raidas once did, across the Thar, a landscape of sand and rocks, parched and dusty grazing grounds. The long barren dunes create an arduous trek across a sterile land. The *tapas* or heat of the desert is the sacrifice to be endured in this place. Mira and Lalita appear tiny and insignificant as they begin to walk across the vast, endless desert like lonely silhouettes in a lost world.

There is tremendous suffering ahead but with determination to reach the abode of the Lord in Vrindavana they begin to walk barefooted across the sands of the desert. Wearing the plain white robes of a mendicant, Mira leaves behind the palace and her cloistered life to become a wanderer, a pilgrim on the path to God, with only Krishna as an anchor to this life.

19. *Tapas*: Crossing the Thar

I am mad with love

And no one understands my plight.

Only the wounded

Understand the agonies of the wounded,

When a fire rages in the heart.

Only the jeweler knows the value of the jewel,

Not the one who lets it go.

In pain I wander from door to door,

But could not find a doctor.

Says Mira: Harken, my Master,

Mira's pain will subside

When Shyam comes as the doctor.

(#70 Alston 62-3)

After many days of endurance, an overwhelming feeling of angst comes over Mira as she experiences the deep sense of loss that all *bhaktas* feel when it seems that the Lord has vanished from the vision of the heart. For in this barren, harsh landscape, Krishna's image is far from her. In the unrelenting heat, her mind begins to wander and she feels interminable pain and desolation for the imagined loss of her Beloved. Even the *murti* is silent and she can no longer hear the Call of the Flute. She is lost in a Wasteland of despair with nothing to follow or guide her, for the sands of the desert shift back and forth like the tide, obscuring the way. It seems to Mira that all paths to the Beloved are closed.

Along the way, the two companions stop at an abandoned wayside shrine that is built at the base of a lone, forlorn tree. The tree is as desiccated as the desert, its shriveled leaves burnt beyond repair and unable to give any shelter to the travelers. The untended altar looks as though no human soul has knelt here in years. No flowers or offerings adorn the bare shrine and there is no sign of any deity residing there. Mira prostrates her exhausted body in the dust, entreating the Dark One to appear. She has nothing to offer Him but her tears, for her throat is so parched she cannot sing or even speak a whispered prayer. And she can no longer feel His presence in any way.

It is said that one must completely let go of the body and ego to merge with Krishna, otherwise He disappears. But despite her unending devotion, Mira is trapped in her physical body amidst the harsh rigors of the journey. Her painfully blistered feet, parched throat, and aching muscles all conspire in creating this illusion of *maya* from which it seems there is no escape. As in her childhood dream, Mira feels herself drying up and withering away. She feels the vast inhumanity of the desert reaching out its dry, skeletal fingers to clutch and entrap her. She fears she will be lost and turned to dust, blowing for all eternity through this barren landscape of desolation, separate from Krishna forever.

At this place of desolation, an ancient crone approaches on foot seemingly out of nowhere. She is as weathered as the landscape and as inscrutable as the shifting dunes of the desert. Around her neck is a charm of the dark skinned flute player. Somehow the amulet looks familiar, like something Mira has seen long ago as a child in the far distant past, or perhaps in a dream. But in her exhausted, disoriented state the image eludes her and she cannot place it in her memory. The Old One tells Mira that she has the look of another who sought her out near this place many years ago. And she offers Mira a reading through the wisdom of the gypsy tarot, a glimpse into her future.

When Mira asks when she will meet her Beloved, the Seer has no answer. For on each shuffle of the deck, the Hanged Man appears, a time of stillness and soul searching. In utter silence, the Old One looks deeply into Mira's soul and can find no words to soften the message. There is still sacrifice and testing ahead and Mira's entire psyche will be turned upside down. Just as the man in the image hangs upside down, so this tree will appear inverted and fling Mira's reality into a new realm and a different perspective. The Gypsy points out the look of serenity on the Hanged Man's face, reminding Mira to find that state of peace within. These words of solace bring Mira a glimmer of hope.

As she leaves, the Crone softly whispers a message to Mira that she must watch for the woman of the Bhilani tribe with the plums who has a gift for her. And perhaps then they will meet again and the cards will speak more fully. As she leaves, she places her amulet of the dark skinned flute player around Mira's neck telling her to keep it close to her heart until it is time to let it go again. And she gives them a vessel of water which remains miraculously cool and ever full for the rest of their journey. Then the Gypsy Crone fades silently into the desert landscape like a phantasm, as if she were a part of the shifting, ever-changing landscape and nothing human.

20. The Heat of Midnight Tears

Listen my friend, this road is the heart opening.

Kissing His feet, resistance broken, tears all night.

If we could reach the Lord through immersion in water.

I would have asked to be born a fish in this life.

If we could reach Him

through nothing but berries and wild nuts,

Then surely the saints would have been monkeys

when they came from the womb!

If we could reach Him by munching lettuce and dry leaves

Then the goats would surely get to the Holy One before us!

If the worship of stone statues could bring us all the way,

I would have adored a granite mountain years ago.

Mirabai says: The heat of midnight tears will bring you to God.

(Bly/Hirshfield 64) Trans Bly

In the evenings after the unrelenting sun finally sinks below the
horizon, the temperature drops abruptly and cold winds blow the
desert sands in a whirlwind, stinging eyes and skin. On some
nights the winds are strangely fierce, moaning and sighing with
a sadness and longing that mirrors Mira's mood. She holds the
amulet close to her breast as if it were the Source of all Life. Hud-
dling together behind a rock with scant protection from the fierce
elements of nature, Mira and Lalita lean into each other for comfort

and warmth. And the companions weep together, releasing the trials of the day.

Mira remembers a time long ago when she was taught in a geography lesson that the ancient name for the Thar is *Murasthali,* the Land of Death. In despair, she realizes that she is very far from the land of the living in this place. Exhausted from her tears, Mira finally drifts into a coma-like sleep. The slumber is so deep it looks as though she has died and descended to the Underworld. The ordeal of the desert has become a life and death crisis. She has become so depleted that she has even lost the ability to shed further tears. She has descended into the deepest abyss, a wintertime of the soul. On this dark of the moon night, even the stars are obscured by thick clouds. And there seems to be no guiding light shining from the heavens to bring hope to a despairing soul. Mira must die to be reborn, so light and life may emerge again.

The face of the *guru* Raidas floats above her as she sleeps, entreating her to remember his words: "When every path seems closed or blocked before you, the Blue God will come without fail to show the Secret Path." Mira hears him faintly, as a nagging entity, when she wants only to escape from the torments of the desert and sleep forever. But the love in his voice warms her will and encourages her to listen.

As she dreams, Surabhi the Sacred Cow, Emissary of Krishna, appears to Mira. "Come", she says, "rest your head in my lap and know the peace of true repose in your Mother's embrace. I will carry you along on your journey. Only you must be willing to surrender to the ride." Her deep brown eyes are warm with compassion and unshed tears of empathy as she cradles Mira in Her arms. Mira is rocked as gently as a new- born infant to a lullaby of peace and protection.

As the tears of Surabhi begin to flow, they moisten and heal Mira's face, body, and spirit. The loving sympathy of the Divine Mother Cow affects Mira so profoundly that she sheds a single tear in response, the only tear that she has left. Like a precious pearl from the ocean, this tiny bit of salty water from the eye of a *Bhakta* is enough to bring the greenness of hope and faith to the desolate landscape and a wounded heart.

Surabhi, the Compassionate One, tells Mira to see her journey through the eyes of her Beloved Lord Krishna, whose blissful and joyous countenance is never clouded by the difficulties of life. Lalita takes on the form of Blue God to shelter and protect her friend, filling her with the remembrance of Krishna's eternal presence. And so, the exhausted Mira wraps her arms around Surabhi's neck and continues the long trek to Vrindavana, unable to tell if she is imagining or actually being carried on the back of the Divine Mother Cow.

21. <u>In the Company of Devotees</u>

My love is reserved for Giridhara Gopal.

And for no-one else.

O ye saints and holy men,

I have seen the world and its ways.

I left brother and relatives

And all I possessed.

Dispensing with worldly shame,

I came to sit with the holy men.

I felt joy in the company of the devotees,

On beholding the world I wept.

I planted the creeper of love

And watered it with my tears.

The King sent me a cup of poison,

I drank it down with joy.

Mira's love has set in deeply,

She accepts whatever comes.

(#18 Alston 40)

As they move further and further into the harsh solitude of the desert, the companions come to a small oasis that provides the shelter of leafy trees and rest for their weary bodies and souls. At first it seems as though a mirage has entered into their numb and exhausted minds to confuse them. As Mira approaches a pool of water she drops with exhaustion and cannot reach it. In her near faint, a shimmering figure comes to her dipping His blue hands in the water and offering her a drink. Such a beautiful child crowned with peacock feathers, or is it a man? Surabhi watches serenely. But when Mira is refreshed, no one is there.

Then, graceful and elegant feminine forms approach. Standing tall and slim, they carry water jugs on their heads and look like goddesses to the eyes of the weary travelers.

The women of the Rajasthani desert are as brightly adorned as tropical birds, bringing color to the monochromatic landscape. Their outfits are dyed in vibrant primary hues and decorated with an intricate pattern of dots and squares. Wearing swinging pleated skirts, long veils that hang down the back to their ankles, and arms full of bangles, they lead Mira and Lalita to the village well and offer the refreshment of food and drink. Surabhi silently leaves them and vanishes into the dream of the desert.

Afterwards, Mira and Lalita are led to a rustic wayside shrine made by the women for the Blue God. Here they see an image of Krishna and Radha together in loving embrace on an altar surrounded by flowers, fruit, charms, and other offerings. The shrine is well tended and loved, used often as a living monument to the devotion of this community. The open-air tableau blends into the greenery of the oasis making the deities come alive like an organic part of nature. Sheltering the shrine, a monumental tree creates a pavilion of refreshing coolness where the devotees can honor the Blue God in comfort.

A young boy, with skin the color of the blue sky, shyly joins Mira for the worship. He would like to sit on Mira's lap and be adored, but first he wants to share some purple plums with her. His winsome manner brings a smile to Mira's face for the first time in many moons. And his innocent and sweet personality allows her to reconnect with her own inner child and put behind her all the hardships she has endured in her travels. She feels a profound love for this little one, as if he was her own beloved son.

Mira notices that the boy is gazing pointedly at the amulet of the dark skinned flute player and looking with intent deeply into her eyes as if trying to alert her to something he wants her to discover herself. She looks closely at the charm from the Old One of the Desert and suddenly, in an epiphany, her memory returns. The image is crystal clear in her mind as she sees her mother laughingly placing it around her neck while they play at a wedding. A wondrous sense of joy washes over her as she imagines her dearly beloved mother's face. And she can feel her departed one's tender, caring presence enfolding her in an embrace.

This time when Mira holds the *murti* to her heart, she hears the divine music of the flute and is moved to express her happiness as a song bubbles forth like a laughing waterfall. The child hears the melody too and laughs in delight. Together Mira and the boy begin to sing and chant, spontaneously creating marvelous harmonies in a duet to the music of Murali the Sacred Flute. The blue child seems to know the melody and words without instruction and the music erupts with a playful, flowing, and effortless ease. Sitting before the altar, Mira again knows Krishna in her heart, for she has the sensation that He is sitting beside her leading the divine music. Soon Mira and the boy are dancing and swaying and the others join in with them in this contagious outpouring of rapture. Like a Phoenix, out of the ashes of suffering has come rebirth.

Mira begins to sing her own *padas*, sharing her heartfelt music. Soon there is a circle of companions who wish to follow Mira as their *guru*. The seekers have shared memories of a past life when they were all *gopis* together and they realize Mira as their Lady Radha reborn. The reunion sparks a great joy among the women for the sisterhood of devotees brings a profound connection to all. Everyone is captivated by the devotion and beauty of Mira and they seek her healing presence. They will follow her on her journey to

Vrindavana.

22. <u>The Wild Woman of the Forest</u>

The wild woman of the forests

Discovered the sweet plums by tasting them

And brought them to her Lord.

She who was neither cultured nor lovely,

She who was filthy in disarrayed clothes,

She of the lowest of castes.

But the Lord, seeing her heart,

Took the ruined plums from her hand.

She saw no difference between low and high,

Wanting only the milk of his presence.

Illiterate, she never studied the teachings-

A single turn of the chariot's wheel

Brought her to knowledge.

Now she is bound to the Storm Bodied One

By gold cords of love, and wanders his woods.

Servant Mira says

Whoever can love like this will be saved.

My Master lifts all that is fallen,

And from the beginning I have been the handmaiden

Herding cows by his side.

(Bly/Hirshfield 56) Trans Hirshfield

Along the way to Vrindavana, the seekers must travel through a wild and lonely mountainous land, the home to the Bhilani tribe.

Deep in the forest, they come to a secluded area where the outcasts of society dwell, far from the centers of civilization and culture. These simple folk of the wilderness live here in complete isolation and peace. At this place, Mira sees a large plum grove beside a pond. The trees are reflected in the shimmering waters and the plums look like precious purple gems both above in the sky and below in the water.

The woman who sits quietly in the shade of the plum tree's heavily laden branches seems to be waiting for her. She is resplendent with the exquisite tribal jewelry of the Bhils. Bell-like hanging earrings, an ornate nose ring, a heavy silver torque that is like a choker hung with coins, and arms full of bangles make up the ensemble. Her clothing is flowing and brightly colored, richly decorated with dots forming a floral pattern. She is heavy with child, weighted down with the fruit of her womb and the heavy jewelry, like the plum trees with their abundant blue fruit. With a smile of innocence and good will, the woman introduces herself as Sabri and offers Mira a half- eaten, dark blue plum from her lap.

For a moment, Mira is taken aback for it seems lacking in courtesy to offer partially eaten food to a stranger. But she is hungry and receives the fruit gratefully. With a sudden, startling insight, she remembers the cryptic message from the Old One in the desert and she notices that Sabri too wears the charm of the dark skinned flute player around her neck. Mira bows to her in recognition of another lover of the Blue God. Sabri returns the obeisance, telling her to eat and remember the sweetness and abundance of all life, for the plums are *prasad*.

Soon a brightly colored caravan of Gypsy wagons drawn by horses approaches. The Travelers have returned home from a *mela* or gypsy fair after many days of camping, music, dance, magic shows, and the bartering of goods. The main wagon halts under a plum tree and the other smaller ones park surrounding it like a wall of protection.

The outside wagons or *vardos* are painted in the stylized images common to Rajasthan with whimsical folk art depicting birds, butter-flies, trees, elephants, flowers. The larger wagon is also ornately decorated but in a different style that sets it apart as a temple or tiny palace, something more royal or sacred. On both sides of the main wagon the Hand of God is depicted, an open palm enclosing an eye in the center, drawn like a henna design. The Divine Eye watches over the One who lives within, protecting her from any unwanted invasion to her privacy. A pair of superbly drawn pea-cocks, painted by a master tribal artist, decorates the entrance. The birds adorn and guard the door, welcoming in all chosen visitors but forbidding all unwanted strangers.

When the latticed *jaali* screen on the top of the door of the main wagon is opened, the Old One from the desert can be seen seated on her throne peering out at Mira with a radiant smile. She is the Queen Matriarch of the Gypsies, dressed in royal garb and covered with jewels. On her lap is the blue skinned boy from the oasis who is the child of Sabri, a royal daughter of the tribe. Recognizing Mira immediately, he claps his hands excitedly, waves and smiles. She notices he is wearing a pair of earrings shaped like crocodiles that hang from his earlobes, ornamenting his enchanting face.

Beckoning to Mira to enter her home on wheels, the Old One has a message to share. As Mira enters the wagon, the veils are drawn and the *jaali* screen closed so none can see or hear their exchange. The Crone has dreamt of Mira sharing the half eaten plums with the priestess Sabri. And like the *guru* Raidas, she has also seen her meditating in Madhuvana, the Forest of Sweetness, deep in communion with the Dark One. By crossing the Thar in her quest for God, Mira has proven her devotion to the *bhakti* path. Now the time is right for a reading of the future; the cards are ready to speak to her.

Sitting on pillows on the wooden floor, they clasp hands across

a low altar-like table and take a moment of quiet to center themselves. The child watches silently, then closes his eyes as if in
prayer while the Gypsy Queen asks Mira to shuffle the cards. When
she is ready, she is to cut the pack in three and turn over the top
card from each pile. First she draws the Hanged Man, the card of
Sacrifice and reversal of vision. Next is the Wheel of Becoming,
which shows the Circle of the *Ban Yatra*, the Journey through the
Twelve Forests that goes round and round like the ever turning
cycles of life. And last is the World, the card of completion and
wholeness, the end of the journey, the end of all desire. Mira sees
the image of She who holds the world in Her hand, offering the ful-
fillment of every heart's dream.

With a knowing smile, the Old One tells Mira she has seen this
same pattern long ago for another seeker much like her. The Crone
says that she must make the *Ban Yatra* pilgrimage of the *mandala*
of the twelve forests and gather the deep blue plums as an offering
for the Dark One. Only after this final initiation will she be allowed
to enter the *Rasa Lila* and Dance with her Lord. She tells Mira to
follow the Secret Path and listen for the call of the flute. And she reminds her of the Hanged Man with the testing ahead under the Asvattha Tree. Some of the women of the tribe agree to go with Mira
to walk the *Ban Yatra* in search of the Dark One. For each seeker
it will be a different journey but in the end, all will arrive in the same

place in the heart of the Blue God.

23. Asvattha, The Cosmic Upside-Down Tree

As Mirabai and her companions approach the outskirts of the sacred lands of Krishna, they see in the distance the City of a Thousand Temples in all its glory. The many spires of the temples of Vrindavana make the city look like the abode of the gods. The town radiates a magical energy that attracts the seekers drawing them quickly to the gates. An ornately decorated and garlanded cow comes to meet them. It is Surabhi, the Sacred One, rejoining the pilgrimage. She walks directly up to Mira and licks her hands and forehead, kissing her in greeting. The tinkling of the cowbells signals the entrance of the pilgrims and as they arrive in Vrindavana, the children run out joyfully to welcome them, recognizing Mira as She who has always been a *gopi*.

One of the children, a dimpled, laughing boy who wears crocodile earrings, welcomes her with a kiss and a garland. He looks so much like Sabri's child; Mira is startled to find him here once again. It seems he appears at every turn of the path. The people have been awaiting the return of the Beloved of Krishna.

The idyllic landscape seems so familiar to Mira, as though she had been here before. To the mundane eye, Vrindavana appears to be an ordinary village. But to the devotees of Krishna it is far more. In the eyes of all seekers, the seasons are always perfect in Vrinda-vana, the groves are lush and ever blooming, the songs of the birds are like melodies from heaven, the colors of nature blossom in all the shades of the rainbow, everyone is joyous and full of love for one another.

Flashes of a transcendental realm, an alternate reality, come in and out of Mira's vision and she is momentarily disoriented, unsure of what is real, what is illusion, and what is part of the Great Mystery. The sensation is like being in two opposing realities at one and the same time, like being split in half both in mind and body. The sound of a flute is calling her, but it is very distant and dream-like. Under one of the trees it appears as though someone is waiting, but Mira sees just a mere glimpse of something blue. The tree itself looks almost as if it were upside-down, like the one in the card of the Hanged Man. She wonders how this can be for she has been told that *Asvattha,* the sacred wish-fulfilling tree, cannot be seen in this world. When she tries to look and listen more closely with her rational mind, all the otherworldly sights and sounds vanish and only ordinary reality remains.

But when she softens her vision and lets go of her ordinary human mode of consciousness, Mira is able to see the bare outline of *As-vattha,* the mythical Tree of Life. The roots of the upside-down tree originate in heaven and the branches come down to earth bringing the blessing of the gods. Everything in this reality is turned around and what is real seems illusion, what is myth becomes reality. Mira knows that under this hallowed tree stands her heart's desire but she must see Him without sight, hear Him without sound, feel Him without touch.

The tree appears to be in early springtime, giving the promise of much more to come. For although the blossoms have emerged, they have not yet fruited into the lush ripeness of summer. The leaves are so fragile and light that the slightest breeze makes them flutter and sing. They seem to whisper messages that cannot be known or expressed in words. As the sun filters in and out of the leaves, it looks to Mira as though hundreds of tiny mirrors are shimmering in a hypnotic dance of light and energy. Reality and illusion, dream and waking state cannot be distinguished under this holy tree, the *Asvattha*.

24. <u>The Middle Path</u>

Mira is dyed deep in the love of Hari

And all else is blocked out.

Wheresoever Krishna leads,

Hither will I follow.

I will not steal, I will harm no one.

How can anyone touch me?

I will not descend from the back of an elephant

to ride upon an ass.

(#25 Alston 43)

Mira has heard that in the forests of Vrindavana dwells a revered *guru*, Jiva, one of the six *goswamis* or Wise Ones. His *ashram* is known throughout all of India and she wishes to receive his blessing before the night of the *Rasa Lila*. But the *guru* will not receive her. He has made a vow never to look upon a woman as part of his sacrifice and asceticism.

Jiva Goswami has become a strict and unbending renunciate. In his isolation, he has lost touch with the beauty and joys of life, becoming weighted down and enmeshed in his studies and teachings. He has not been in the company of women or children for many years. And he has not heard the sound of laughter or received any touch of affection for far too long. Surrounded by students who revere and fear him, he has become an unapproachable ascetic.

Mira is surprised when she is informed of his refusal. At the gates of his *ashram*, within his hearing, she states that she was taught that the only male in Vrindavana is Krishna, for all His worshippers are *gopis*. She has received this wisdom from her *guru* Raidas and asks: "Are not all souls female before God? Krishna is the only male; He alone is the Creator and active principle. All devotees, both men and women, are female, being receptive and responsive." Mira's eloquent words stir the mind and heart of the *goswami* and a spark is ignited in the core of his spirit. What has become rigid and tightly bound within him begins to unwind and he is humbled to recognize the truth of her vision.

Mira is invited into his *ashram* and temple. She can see that something in Jiva has been depleted and needs healing and so she offers her music for the *puja*. Tears roll down the elder *goswami's* face as he moves beyond the academics of his faith into the *bhakti* for Krishna that Mira expresses in her songs. His entire appearance seems to soften and grow younger as he undergoes this epiphany. Coldness and judgment unthaw, replaced by warmth and tolerance. Rigidity, stiffness, and wrinkles become supple flesh that glows with health. By the time the worship is ended, Jiva is smiling and relaxed as he gives Mira his blessing.

The Blue God comes to the Goswami then as a voice in his mind. He wants the *guru* to give Mira a message. Jiva relays the words of Krishna telling Mira she is going to encounter a golden hued saint who will give her further guidance in her quest. This magical being is both male and female combined at the same time to create a soul that goes beyond gender into the ultimate unity of all things.

The next person Mira meets is certainly not the Golden One fore-told by Jiva Goswami. At a gathering in the groves the following day, an impromptu *kirtana* is being offered. Mira is called upon to participate and she sings several of her *padas*. In the crowd, she notices an unconventional, rather eccentric looking but handsome man dressed in a flowing patchwork robe of many colors with his long uncut hair in a topknot. He is so riveted by Mira's music he appears to be absorbed in an ecstatic trance. Wearing a beaded choker formed from stems of *tulasi*, tiny bells jingle from his ankles, chiming softly whenever he moves. His way of walking is fluidly sensuous and he has an aura of great attractiveness which draws the attention of many in the crowd of devotees. Carrying several unusual musical instruments with him, his carefree, whimsical man-ner is charming and charismatic.

When the minstrel comes forth to sing, the music he plays is a wild outpouring of emotion. His voice is by turn joyous with ecstasy, sharp with sarcasm, as softly suggestive as a lover's caress and full of the deepest longing. The bard accompanies himself with a one stringed drone and with the other hand beats a little drum. The music sounds extemporaneous, as if it were being invented in the here and now. The enigmatic verses he sings tell of the Way of Love and the *Maner Manush* or He who lives in the Heart:

> My mind goes wandering in the garden of Krishna.
> There you will go and surrender your heart
> To a world of bliss.
> In this garden are abundant fruits.
> There is one that is invisible.
> Those who have tasted it become as if mad;
> It fulfills their desires and ambitions.
> Only those who have tasted it know its name.
>
> (Bhattacharyya 29)

This minstrel is a Baul from Bengal whose only religion is music. After he plays, a group of similarly garbed men comes forth and bows at his feet as if he were a revered saint. Others in the gathering whisper that the young bard is indeed their main *guru*. They say that his followers honor and believe in him literally as Krishna in human form. The name Baul means "He who is carried by the Wind." He is a free spirit, a Wanderer of the desert with no home, on a quest to quench his intense longing for oneness with the divine, much like Mira. He belongs to no organized orthodox religion or *caste* and follows no dogma, loving freedom and spontaneity above all things.

The Baul approaches Mira the following day, for he has been taken by her music and her beauty. In Mira, he sees divinity through earthly love, for the Bauls believe that woman embodies the mystery of the universe and holds the key to liberation in her body as the temple of the divine. The minstrel says he has had a marvelous vision telling him to make love with her so that they may reach the divine together. He wants her to be his *Khepi* or consort and wander the desert with him playing music for alms. When Mira declines, telling him she is married to Krishna, the Baul tells her that he is Krishna and continues to make overtures to her in public amidst all her companions and the many other seekers in Vrindavana. He is playful but insistent as he sings a song to her with a heart full of longing:

> Put the feet of woman upon your head;
> For without her, nothing moves!
> Haven't you noticed
> That all the holy shrines
> Are at the feet of woman?
> She is the Wish-granting Tree
> Of which I hear in the *sadhu* tradition.

Having stumbled on orthodox teachings,

I fail to glimpse her.

In the form of the woman of the house,

She is the Mother of all beings.

In her sensuous aspect

She fulfills all wishes.

(Bhattacharyya 40)

The Baul's path is the extreme opposite of what Jiva Goswami once followed. In his playful yet provocative way, the minstrel has made a mockery of the dry asceticism, rigid adherence to scripture, and celibate life styles of the orthodox. He has a wicked sense of humor and no qualms about expressing his opposition to the mainstream of society. Although this man appears to be sincerely devout, this is not the path for Mira. She must follow the Middle Way. In her mind, Krishna's voice is echoing, coming straight from the *murti* as she holds it close. She can see Him winking at her in delight as a plan forms in her thoughts. For although Mira respects the minstrel's beliefs, she must find a way to end his desire.

Mira agrees to grant the Baul's desire and prepares a fragrant bed of flowers soft with cushions and pillows for his comfort and pleasure. But, she says they must enjoy each other before the other devotees and before her *murti* of Krishna in order to please the Blue God. At once, the inanimate *murti* seems to come alive. The

172

Blue God shows both His forbidding and protective aspects through His facial expressions and body gestures. Without a word being said and no actions taken, the Baul understands that the bond between Mira and Krishna does not include him, and bows at her feet in respect. Mira wonders if perhaps the Dark One has disguised Himself in the form of the minstrel to test her heart.

25. <u>Chaitanya Mahaprabhu, The Golden-Skinned Avatar</u>

My Beloved has come home with the rains,

And the fire of longing is doused.

Now is the time for singing, the time of union.

At the first thunderclap,

Even the peacocks open their tails

with pleasure and dance.

Giridhara is in my courtyard,

and my wandering heart has returned.

Like lilies that blossom under the full moon's light,

I open to him in this rain:

Every pore of my body is cooled.

Mira's separation and torment are over.

He who comes to those who love has remembered

His promise.

(Bly/Hirshfield 50) Trans Hirshfield

Some days later during her morning meditation, Mira sees in a vision a beautiful golden being whose rich, lyrical voice is calling her further into the forest realms of Krishna. He is graceful and androgynous, matching the description in Jiva Goswami's message. The Golden One stands before Mira in shining splendor, glowing like the sun. She has heard about this great teacher who *was* prophesied and will appear in the guise of a devotee of the Lord to deliver a new message of liberation and love to the world. She hears his words of inspiration spoken in a melodious, deep voice.

> The chanting of Krishna's name purifies the mirror of the soul,
> subsides the agonizing fire of the material mind,
> and sprouts the bliss of Krishna's divine love
> that brings complete divine contentment at every step of life.
> Such an experience of Krishna's love
> exceeds all the blissful experiences of all the other divine abodes.
> Chaitanya Mahaprabhu *Siksastaka*

By permission Nikhileshwari Devi (http//www.bhakti-yoga-meditation.com)

Mira is told by this golden being that he is the direct incarnation of the Blue God. His purpose on earth at this time is to reveal *kirtana*, the chanting of the sacred names of Krishna. He whispers his name telling her that He is sometimes called Gaura, the Golden One. Within this great being is the embodiment of Radha's love for Krishna. But at the same time, He is Krishna, appearing also in the form of a devotee. In Gauri is this unique combination and He comes to this world to give the love between Radha and Krishna to all beings. In Mira's vision, he tells her that she must go to worship in Mathura at the Temple of Krishna's Birth on Janmastami, the day of the Lord's birth. There she will find the way to gain her heart's desire and continue her journey of transformation.

Later when Mira mentions the visitation to other seekers and describes his unforgettable song-like voice, she is told that this is Sri Chaitanya Mahaprabhu, the golden skinned saint whose name means "One Who awakens the Spirit of Krishna in the Heart." He has taken up residence in the forests of Vrindavana and rediscovered many of the lost locations of Krishna's pastimes in Braj as part of the Ban Yatra pilgrimage. Now he is waiting for Mira to come to him for his blessings and gifts. Mira and her companions hope to be led by this holy saint through the forests and land of Krishna's life. Perhaps when they have completed the Ban Yatra all will be as the Gypsy said and they will be allowed to enter the Great Circle Dance.

The pilgrims go to Mathura, the birthplace of Krishna. It is *Janmastami,* the birthday of the Dark One. In every temple in the city, the celebration is in progress. At the time and place ordained in her vision of the Golden One, the seekers are ushered into the temple by the clanging of brass bells and the chanting of the many names of God. An ecstatic, charismatic *pandit* leads the worship. He is singing and dancing with a tremendously contagious energy of devotion. Seeing his golden hued skin, hearing his distinctive singing voice, and recognizing the essence of her Lord Krishna within this soul, Mira knows he is the great *sadhu* Chaitanya Mahaprabhu. Speaking in his uniquely musical voice, she hears words that mirror exactly her own personal experience of Krishna:

Chanting the name of the Lord,

one should be so engrossed in God while singing His name

that tears start rolling out of the eyes;

speech may grow ecstatic

and the body starts feeling spiritual and passionate.

The best and easiest way to get purged is by chanting the name of God.

Anyone can chant the name of the Lord anytime and anywhere.

There is no barrier of time and place.

Sri Chaitanya Mahaprabhu

By permission Abhilash(http//www.hindu-blog.com)

After the *kirtana* is complete, peacocks outside of the temple begin emitting their weird and startling cry, the herald of rain. And the monsoon begins to arrive in an exhilarating storm of sound and energy, the auspicious sign needed to begin the *Ban Yatra*. The sounds of nature draw the worshippers outdoors through the temple gates to see a purple sky and clouds that are swollen with the life giving moisture of Mother Nature. Lighting thunders in awe inspiring and dramatic flashes of electric display and deafening accents.

Mira has been waiting for this time and she weeps with joy as the storm begins to release itself in torrents of passionate energy, revitalizing the landscape. Becoming one with the monsoon, she mirrors the release it brings in her tears and is refreshed and rejuvenated. As the monsoon soaks the parched earth, the land turns green before their eyes.

Celebrating, the worshippers run in sheer delight through the pouring rain to bathe in the healing waters of the Yamuna River. At the end of the path, a series of steps takes them down to the water. The rains from the monsoon mix with the river waters drenching and purifying the seekers for their sojourn into the forests of Braj.

At the Yamuna River, Mira and her companions make the special vow called *sankalpa* before Chaitanya, pledging that they will complete the entire journey of the Ban Yatra as prescribed in the sacred texts. They make little boats out of palm leaves, fill them with lotus petals, fruits, and tiny lit candles, and set them out into the water as an offering. In the evening, the area will be dotted with dozens of little lights in honor of the pilgrimage. In return, Chaitanya agrees to guide them through the twelve petals of the Braj *mandala*, the *Ban Yatra*.

26. <u>Bala Krishna, The Divine Child</u>

In the evening, Mira joins the many devotees of Krishna who gather in multitudes and descend into the darkness of the prison site where their Lord first incarnated. In honor of Janmastami, the local Ras Troupe will perform a *lila* or play on the birth of Krishna. Native Brahmin boys from Braj play the parts and have been trained over many generations by the Rasdharis, the musicians and teachers who accompany the play.

When they are costumed, these boys become consecrated beings entering into the personality of the gods to create a living theater. In this combination of theater and worship, play and ritual, the audience becomes an essential part of the transcendent experience. Attending Ras Lila is the same as entering the temple for worship, a journey into the heart of God within the self. Krishna is the main actor, the *avatar* of God who comes down to engage in His cosmic and romantic love play.

The curtain is drawn as the excited chatter of the onlookers becomes complete silence and the play begins. Before Mira's eyes, the birth of the eighth avatar of Vishnu in the depths of the prison, and all the attending magic of His incarnation, takes place. For her, there is the overwhelming sense that she is re-living the experience from another time.

Mira sees the mother Devaki giving birth, and watches as the entire world falls into a sleep so deep that Vasudeva, the father, can carry his tiny son away to safety, far from the evil intentions of King Kansa. As if by some miracle, the prison doors open to release them, for God can never be incarcerated or contained in any way. A blue mist cloaks them in secrecy so none may see the escape.

Vasudeva must cross the monsoon swollen Yamuna with his precious bundle and bring Him to the foster parents Nanda and Yasoda who will, without knowledge of His true identity, guard and protect Him. The audience watches with bated breath, silent prayers, and frightened tears, hoping that a terrible disaster will not occur. But the Divine Child touches the overflowing waters of the Yamuna and they settle in peace to let Him pass safely to His new home. Great joy and relief is felt by all the onlookers, who are united and bonded in the suspense of witnessing the wondrous birth and escape. The play ends with *arati* and the seekers arise as one roaring an emotional approval at the arrival of the young Lord into their midst.

The Divine Child is especially revered and adored by the people. Even as an infant, He has the power, with one smile, to lift His devotees out of their bodies and their everyday lives into an ecstasy of joyous abandon and love for Him. And now, the entire audience is given this divine experience of unconditional love and acceptance. All unhappiness, negativity, and ill will are banished in an instant by the sweet laughter of Bala Krishna.

27. <u>The Blue God Speaks</u>

After the players have left the stage, there is an extended time of silence. The song of a flute is softly calling and when Mira opens her eyes only the child Krishna remains before her. Then a blue haze materializes around the stage enveloping the boy until he is no longer visible. She can imagine the Goddess Maya placing Her Veils of Illusion over what seems on the surface to be an ordinary play on the life of Krishna. Now the spectators will truly enter the temple, the inner sanctum of the Divine.

The blue mist no longer obscures the scene and the child has disappeared. Transformed by some miracle, a massive altar full of flowers, fruit, and offerings has taken his place. Standing before them now is a beautiful blue skinned man crowned with peacock feathers, smiling at His devotees with tender affection. Unlike the multi-armed deities of Vedic myth, He has only two arms just like any human being. He is both God and human at the same time, fully accessible to all who come to Him with love and devotion. At least this is what appears to Mira.

The Blue God begins to play His flute and each person present has a slightly different experience. For some, Maya has obscured all vision and there is nothing there at all. For others, God is indeed present, but they cannot look upon Him in His brilliance. And for those fortunate and blessed souls, God has come down in human form to be on earth with them. In every vision, the music has a different quality and character. In turn it is playful and child-like, celebratory and exultant, serene yet full of unresolved yearning. For those few who are unable to open to the visual experience, the flute sounds forceful and a little strident, cajoling them to let go of the limitations of ordinary reality and see God. Despite these differences, all present can hear the sublime music in some form, all are held captive under its spell of celestial harmony.

On this exalted occasion, the birthday of God, it is tradition that Krishna comes forth and gives a speech of inspiration, called the *Pravacan*. Some explain the experience in terms of an enactment, a part of the play. But for others, it is the Lord Himself who is speaking directly to them using the player as a channel. No matter what they are experiencing, the magic of the moment will touch each seeker's heart. Though the form or vision may vary, there is no one who cannot receive the blessings of the Blue God.

For one who worships Me, giving up all his activities unto Me
and being devoted to Me without deviation,
engaged in devotional service and always meditating upon Me,
who has fixed his mind upon Me,

for him, I am the swift deliverer from the ocean of birth and death.

Lord Krishna Bhagavad Gita 12.6-7

(Prabhupada 520)

The audience of devotees is exultant hearing these words. Many are weeping, others laughing; the joy is cosmic. Strangers embrace each other like members of one family and everyone is feeling the same universal, unconditional love emanating from their beloved Blue God. This love flows around the entire room of people and returns once again to their Eternal Beloved where it is sent out into the universe for the benefit of all beings. The mood is one of ecstasy and rapture. As one, the entire group of devotees prostrates themselves, no longer able to look upon this brilliant vision of divinity. Time stands still, all sound and movement ceases, and when the people begin to arise, the stage is empty, the vision gone.

28. <u>Ban Yatra: The Forest Pilgrimage</u>

The next day Mira and her companions begin to walk the Ban Yatra, the pilgrimage of the twelve forests. This is the Secret Path through the Tall Grass, where the beginning is the end and all passageways lead to the same place in the heart of God. They will visit many of the places of Krishna's pastimes, going through a continual process of purification by bathing in the waters of the many ponds and circumambulating the sacred sites. At the end of the Ban Yatra in the center of the *mandala* is a Garden of Paradise with the sacred Cosmic Tree holding the universe together. And under this tree stands the Blue God awaiting all who seek Him.

The journey of the *Ban Yatra* begins in Madhuvana, the Forest of Sweetness, where the *gopis* once gathered honey for their Beloved Lord. The delicate perfume of the honey permeates the grove, attracting the seekers like bees to nectar. It is at this very site that Raidas first pictured Mira in his dream from long ago. And now he is here to join the pilgrimage, keeping his promise to her. He is delighted to see that the *murti* he gave to Mira as a child is still with her. Mira's pleasure in the *Ban Yatra* is made compete with both her *sakhi* Lalita and her *guru* Raidas as companions.

The Ban Yatra is a pilgrimage of joy and community. The seekers do not focus on sacrifice, asceticism, or deprivation, though the long walk can be hard, but rather on celebrating life. For Mira, it is a stark contrast to the journey across the Thar Desert where she felt only despair and separation. Here she is part of something larger than herself and feels as though she is a member of a loving family. She can feel the presence of her long departed and dearly loved parents with her as she remembers the story of their journey on the *Ban Yatra* to receive Krishna's blessing, her life.

It is a precious gift to walk in the company of the Lord. Through love of Krishna, the participants become brothers and sisters, sharing the sacred, instructional, playful, and challenging aspects of the long walk through the twelve forests. All day long everyone is in high spirits, singing, chanting, dancing and frolicking along like uninhibited children in the festive procession. No one ever seems tired or unhappy. Krishna's everlasting delight in His devotees and in all of life has brought the group enthusiasm, an endless energy, and an eager appetite for this once in a lifetime adventure.

Chaitanya instructs the devotees on the various pastimes of the Lord at each sacred site as they sit under the Banyan trees in the peaceful groves of the forests. Often the Ras troupe arrives to enact the wondrous saga of Krishna's childhood. Like chapters in a sacred novel or an adventurous fairy tale, the forest provides a tableau for the story and the characters become living, breathing entities. Many of the woodland animals are attracted to the gathering of pilgrims and they seem to sit in awe of the miraculous stories and teachings that are offered. As Mira listens to the tales and walks along the path, she is entering into the life of Krishna and becoming a participant in His play. Her experience on a personal level is what brings the Blue God to life in the here and now of the forest groves.

In Braj, all of nature is magical. It is a dream landscape imbued with the moods and legends of Krishna. The sunrise shimmers on the waters in the early mornings and at night the moon is reflected like a mirror of glass in the many ponds and lakes the seekers pass. The stars sparkle like diamonds and sapphires, lighting up the evening sky. Even the multi-colored hues of the pilgrim's apparel look like the jeweled rainbows of nature, creating a festive sight to match the high spirits of the seekers. In the evening, just as the lotus opens during the day and closes at night in the cool air, so the lotus petals of the *mandala* draw together as they sleep to wrap the pilgrims close in the protective embrace of the Blue God.

29. <u>Divine Ferrier</u>

Guide this little boat over the waters,

What can I give you for fare?

Our mutable world holds nothing but grief,

Bear me away from it.

Mira cries: Dark One-0

Take this little boat to the far shore,

Put an end to coming and going.

(Schelling 62)

As a break from the long walk of the Ban Yatra, the companions decide they would like to take a short pleasure ride on one of the lakes. It is a beautiful clear day, the waters are calm, and there is not even one cloud in the sky. Soon an attractive young boy approaches Mira and her group, offering to ferry them over the lake. He shows them his modest wooden boat, simple and unadorned, but clean and comfortable with cushions for seating.

The boy exudes confidence and friendliness. His skin is as dark as the color of purple plums and it looks soft as velvet. They agree to ride with him despite his youth, for he has such a winning manner and a captivating smile, all dimples and sunshine. Once they are aboard, the boy takes out a flute and plays a sprightly melody for them, setting the mood for a charming and relaxing excursion.

But when they are in the middle of the pond, the boy stops rowing and feigns exhaustion. He acts sulky and even sheds a few tears, telling them he must be placated with treats and sweet words, before he can continue and bring them ashore. Though the words are unspoken, what he really hungers for is love. There is a secret, hidden smile in his eyes as though he is enjoying some great cosmic joke.

When his wishes are not immediately granted, the lake begins to churn with a sudden wild energy as though all of Nature has been aroused and made angry. The waters heave and lurch like a tempest until the companions begin to feel seasick. The sky becomes dark and overcast, lightning flashes, and a deluge threatens to inundate and overwhelm the little boat. Mother Nature is having a temper tantrum. The occupants of the boat begin to shiver with the sudden cold draft of the wind that lashes the frail craft back and forth and they feel themselves to be adrift in an unknown universe. The strength of the wind and the wild waves threaten to throw the little boat off course into uncharted waters.

The child, who seems strangely familiar to Mira, has a shy smile on his face and watches his passengers closely. He secretly winks at Mira as if to say there is no danger, only a bit of mischief from a child. After he is given all the love and compliments, kisses and assorted sweets they can offer, Mira becomes consciously aware of what she had not noticed before. The child is the dusky blue hue of the Lord, wears the crocodile earrings, and has a crown of peacock feathers set jauntily upon his head. He looks deeply into the eyes of each seeker and they see his divine nature. Kissing the forehead of each departing pilgrim, an unspoken blessing is given and received. The waters have become tranquil once again, the sky clear and brilliantly blue, and Mira recognizes the playful game He has led them on.

Whoever the Divine Ferrier carries across the waters is taken on a mystic barge through the Veil of Maya and casts off to the distant shores of life's other side. Arriving on the far banks, the pilgrims feel as though they have crossed the Ocean of Becoming to arrive at the Promised Land, guided by God Himself. For although the waters are now calm and unruffled, they sense that they have moved through a formidable barrier in reaching the Heart of Enlightenment in the Mystic Circle Dance.

30. Beloved of Krishna

As they walk along together, the pilgrims are learning the nature
of *lila* or the cosmic play of life, being in the moment, having no
destination except for union with the Lord. And so once again they
return to the source, the beginning of the *mandala*. But the place
is not the same as it was for the pilgrims have been transformed by
the journey and are no longer who they were at the start of the *Ban
Yatra*.

Here at the heart center of the Braj *mandala*, is a Garden of Paradise where the Blue God eternally resides. Now the Call of His
flute is heard and the devotees begin to gather. For on this magic
night, those who have passed the initiation, whose eyes have been
opened, can see the Blue God waiting under the mystical *Asvattha*
and hear the song of Murali.

That evening, the full moon rises luminous and golden in the month
of Shavrana and the time for the Maharasa Lila has arrived. The pilgrims keep vigil until midnight, singing *bhajans* and *kirtans* of deep
devotion. Maya, the Veil of Illusion, has cloaked the scene in a blue
mist, keeping out those who are unprepared to enter and partake of
this spiritual magic. She reveals the circle only to the *Bhaktas*, the
Lovers of God.

And now Radha arrives to lead the *gopis* into the sacred circle. As Mira gazes upon her golden countenance, she can see Chaitanya blending with Radha's essence. As Krishna is considered to be the only male in the universe, everyone else, both male and female, is a *gopi*. One of the seekers has an uncanny resemblance to her *guru* Raidas in his spirit form. Another *gopi* seems to have the persona of Jiva Goswami, the sage from the Groves of Vrindavana. Even the Baul from Bengal is here in the graceful shape of his *khepi* or consort. The Guardian of the Circle is the old Gypsy Crone accompanied by Surabhi the Sacred Mother Cow.

On this most hallowed night, the groves of Vrindavana sparkle with a vitality beyond the ordinary. The entire world is intoxicated with love for the Dark Lord. Murali is calling, entreating the seekers to join in the Dance. The Seekers are greeted and welcomed at the threshold of the Magic Circle by the comely dark boy who wears the crocodile earrings. He garlands them and marks them with the *tilaka*. Their eyes are anointed with the salve of pure love so they may see and experience the sublime. Soon *Shyamsundara*, the Lord of the Beautiful Evenings, will appear.

In the blink of an eye, the young boy vanishes and The Blue God is standing before them under the sacred *Asvattha* tree at the center of the circle. As the devotees cross over the invisible boundary into the Sacred Circle, the tree blossoms and fruits, producing plums of a deep blue color. The seekers have reached the Heart of Enlightenment. Picking the plums, Mira tastes several first to choose the very sweetest before giving it to Krishna. As they laugh together with joy, Mira feeds her Beloved the sanctified offering of plums as a gift that is accepted with delight. Krishna's magical touch has created an unending supply of perfect fruit out of Mira's offering. In Divine Communion, He gives this *prasad* to every *gopi*. Tasting the sweetness of life, they each take the sacrament of the Dark One knowing that none need ever hunger or thirst in His realm. The Blue God has opened the Secret Path as Raidas had promised

In this Circle of Love, all of time and space are contained and protected within the boundaries. Everything stands still and the entire universe seems to stop, watching in awed silence. The regular movement of time is stretched into eternity through the mystic powers of Krishna. And yet, for all within this numinous realm, it seems but a brief moment. The mystery that encompasses all things, bigger than anything the human mind can begin to imagine is made manifest and real. The seekers dance into the luminous blue light of Krishna and become One. Everything in the universe is united in the One Source, in His arms, in the heart of God.

31. <u>Dwarka, the Lost City of Many Gates</u>

When the time of the Rasa Lila has passed, Krishna speaks to Mira through the *murti* and instructs her to go to Dwarka. Located on the western coast of the Arabian Sea. Dwarka, The City of Many Gates, is the place associated with Krishna's reign as an earthly king. The name Dwarka means the Doorway to Eternal Bliss. The Blue God built the city for His people as a haven of peace after a long period of strife and war. And Krishna has told them there are many gates to God and by whatever gate His *bhaktas* come to Him, at that Gate will He stand to greet them.

In legend it is said that Krishna was given a gift of this land from the sea to build His legendary city. It was known as the Golden City so magnificent were its many palaces and *mandirs* of gold, silver, and precious gems. The radiance of the city was glowing like the charismatic face of Krishna and shed its warmth and light upon the ocean for all to see. In her God given vision, Mira sees everything as it was in the time of Krishna's reign.

But Dwarka became the Lost City, the Submerged City. After Krishna had finished with His work for this incarnation and departed His body, the waters reclaimed the land in a huge tidal wave. Perhaps it was at the Lord's command that the city was destroyed, for there was something of His *lila* in the ease and play of its demise. Arjuna tells of watching the forces of Nature overwhelm Dwarka in a matter of moments and then settle back into serenity as though nothing had happened and the city had never been. Before Mira's startled eyes, the golden city of Dwarka is inundated and erased from the surface of the earth. Later the site was rebuilt by Lord Krishna's descendants and this is the city that Mira will come to.

Coming back to this time and place, Mira finds that Krishna has given her the conch-shell seal, which is possessed by every inhabitant of Dwarka as a mark of identity. She decides to wear it as a talisman around her neck. Now Mira is ready to take her *gopi* self to His city and offer her songs as a *seva* or service to the people. Once again, Mira begins a pilgrimage, this time accompanied both by Lalita and Raidas as well as the women from the Thar Desert. It is a journey of celebration for they are coming home traveling as a family of devotees by caravan with the gypsy nomads of the Bhilani tribe until they reach the sea. Because they want to approach Dwarka by water to experience the magical view, they continue by boat.

As she enters the city, Mira imagines she can see the radiant glow of Old Dwarka with its many gateways, opening to her. Wearing the conch shell seal as her right to enter the city, she and her friends are welcomed at the waters by the residents. As Mira walks up the steps from the beach landing and through the gateway to the splendid temple, the sound of a conch bellows forth to announce a celebration of major proportion, for the Beloved of Krishna has returned to the Golden City by the Sea.   The people of Dwarka welcome Mira, hailing her as Radha, foremost of *Bhaktas*. She has finally come home.

In time, Mira takes up residence at the Krishna Temple on Bet Dwarka, an island in the bay so closely surrounded by water on all sides that the waves can be heard during the worship. After the destruction of Dwarka, this tiny island was all that remained of the original city. The only access to this secluded place is by ferry. The simple boat is packed and crowded with passengers hanging off the sides, but spirits are high as the pilgrims approach the beach.

Mira makes the *mandir* into a beautiful, intimate sanctuary surrounded by gardens and orchards full of purple plum trees. The constant murmur of the waves can be heard within during the worship. Raidas and Lalita attend her, along with many of the sister seekers who traveled the Ban Yatra together. Within the temple, one can always hear the sound of music and partake in the joy of personal communion with God. From the edge of the waters, the golden silhouette of Dwarka City can be seen in the far distance like a miniature painting from Rajasthan.

Time passes and Mira's life is one of devotion and song. Bet Dwarka is a place where everything is music and everything is Krishna; nothing else exists. Many come on pilgrimage to receive *darshan* of Mira. And some find their love for the Blue God here in this island community of devotees and decide to stay to serve in the temple.

32. Everything Perishes

But nothing ever remains forever the same with the passage of time. Everything perishes; only the Indestructible One remains. After many years of peace and harmony, Mira receives another vision from the *murti*, a prophetic message from Krishna. *Pandits* from Chittor will be arriving in Dwarka to bring her back to the royal family. It has been said that the Sisodiyas are suffering punishment and defeat in the war with the Moguls because of their treatment of Mira, who is now revered by the people as a saint. The family, in their superstition and ignorance, believes that the return of Mira to Chittor will stem the tide of destruction, breaking the power of the siege. Even Vikram, through royal decree, grudgingly states he is willing to offer her refuge and sanctuary.

The men from the palace arrive, demanding that Mira comes back with them. When she refuses, they begin a hunger strike. And so the tender-hearted Mira agrees to go with them and return to her old life. Her only request is to be granted one last evening alone in the temple of her Beloved Krishna.

Speaking from the lips of the *murti*, Krishna tells Mira more about the deepest, most secret meaning of *Asvattha*, the Cosmic Tree of

Life:

The real form of this tree cannot be perceived in this world.

No one can understand where it ends, where it begins, or where its foun-

dation is.

But with determination one must cut down this tree with the weapon of

detachment.

So doing, one must seek that place from which, having once gone, one

never returns,

And there surrender to that Supreme Personality of Godhead

from whom everything has begun and in whom everything is abiding since

time immemorial.

Bhagavad Gita 15.3-4 (Prabhupada 601)

And so Mira understands that she must begin to prepare herself to ascend to the realm that has no return. There she will find the place that is illuminated neither by sun nor moon nor fire but is lit only with the radiance of the Lord. This is the Dark One's highest dwelling place and once she has gained entrance she will not return again to the cycle of transmigration and will merge with her beloved Lord. Mira accepts the message completely and she is ready without question to cut away all of her attachments to this life.

At midnight, Mira enters the temple to begin a *puja* to the Lord assisted by Lalita and Raidas. The Old One from the desert is

199

also present for this final rite in Dwarka and Mira returns the amulet of The Dark-skinned Flute Player to its Keeper. The ritualists draw a *yantra* on the floor to call down the Blue God as they chant the Hare Krishna Mantra. The love between the companions is unspoken, felt and communicated not with language but through the warmth of emotion and long comradeship. Outside the temple doors, a single white cow with brown eyes guards the entrance.

The shrill and eerie cry of the peacocks that have come to surround the *mandir* can be heard inside the shrine. Heralding a storm, suddenly the winds have come up and lightning flashes in the skies. Something primal and supernatural is being stirred up in the cosmos. It is the full moon night of the Rasa Lila and now an eclipse covers the golden moon in darkness as the heavens release their pounding rain in lamentation of an impending loss.

When all is in readiness, Mira is left alone by her companions to make the final invocation for calling Krishna to the *yantra* and completing her farewell to Him. In a voice full of deep yearning, she sings one of her most stirring, heartfelt *padas* to Him. With complete detachment, Mira cuts off the braid of her beautiful long hair in one tremendous sweep of sacrifice and tosses it in reverence on the floor in front of the *murti*. In her prayer Mira sings:

O Jogi, do not depart.

Behold, I fall at Your feet, Your slave.

Strange is the path of love and devotion!

Explain to me its intricacies

Before you depart.

I am laying a pyre of fragrant aloe and sandalwood.

Light it with Your own hand

Before you depart.

When I am burnt to a heap of ashes

Smear them on your body

Before you depart.

Let my light dissolve in your light

Before you depart.

(#46 Alston 53)

As Mira walks into the center of the circle, the temple begins to fill with a mysterious blue light. Bells clang wildly and all the candles in the sanctuary burst into flame. Holding the *murti* of Krishna to her heart, it begins to transform into a life sized, physical being standing in front of Mira in the midst of the *yantra*. The Lord has come at last to dance to the music of His devotee's *padas*. Flute music is sounding in the temple though none are present to hear except Mira. And she seems to dissolve into His embrace.

No witnesses are present to explain what has taken place. Only the Devotee and Her Lord may know the sacred experience. Mira has cut all ties to this world and passed beyond the Veil of Maya. She has walked through the Secret Door into the realm of divine illumination and reached the Heart of Enlightenment. At this exact moment, the clouds part and the radiant full moon shines on the *mandir* once again in peace and harmony as though the storm was an illusion that never was. And now, a woman's soaring voice can be heard accompanied by the flute.

In the morning when the men arrive at the temple to take Mira away, the white cow still stands outside guarding the entrance. The peacocks are nowhere to be seen. The doors must be broken down for they are mysteriously locked from the inside and Mira is gone. Her *saari* is draped over the *murti* of Krishna along with her gleaming braid of dark hair. Mira has shed all of herself; she has melded and merged with the Dark One, attaining her life's purpose, union with the divine. The Blue God has opened The Secret Path.

At least this is the story of Mira's disappearance the Brahmins will tell the royal court when they return to Chittor alone. Lalita calmly enters the shrine and shows no emotion over the absence of Mira. Perhaps she knows the secret of her disappearance or trusts fully in her *bhakti* without needing an answer. Along with Mira, the essence of Krishna is gone, for the *murti* is pale and still. Only an empty shell remains. Krishna has gone to join His Beloved in *Nirvana*.

Over time the statue is mysteriously lost and a legend evolves claiming it has dissolved into dust like the grains of sand in the Thar Desert. There seems to be no trace of it left on earth and the world is full of darkness. And yet, it returns at the right time and place to whoever can seek, find, and hold it. And some say that if it is found, the *murti* may speak and bestow blessings on the people of the earth, but only if One who can hear the divine music of Murali holds it to her heart..

Not long after Mira's disappearance, Dwarka is once again re-claimed by the sea. The purpose of this sacred city has been com-pleted for another incarnation and through the power of the Lord it no longer exists in the mundane realm. The future will show that Dwarka would be submerged and rebuilt many times, reborn time and time again in the great cycle of birth, life, death, and rebirth.

33. <u>Postlude: A Realm Beyond Going</u>

Let us go to a realm beyond going,

Where death is afraid to go,

Where the high- flying birds alight and play,

Afloat in the full lake of love.

There they gather- the good, the true-

To strengthen an inner regimen,

To focus on the dark form of the Lord

and refine their minds like fire.

Garbed in goodness- their ankle bells-

They dance the dance of contentment

There where the love of the Dark One comes first

And everything else is last.

(Hawley/Juergensmeyer 140) Caturvedi, no. 193)

Thus ends the legend of Mirabai as it is told in the chronicles of history. The Brahmins return to the Court of Chittor with their mission unfulfilled. But perhaps, it was indeed fulfilled according to the destiny and horoscope of Mira. Everyone wondered and imagined many marvelous and incomprehensible things.

No story is ever complete in the endless cycle of life, death, and rebirth. The Wheel continues to turn as the seasons change, and the years pass by. The vibrations set forth by Mira are heard to this day in her music and poetry and in all the arts that express the joys and sorrows of life and the yearning of the human heart for the Divine. For this is the essential nature of Art.

Lalita carefully collected all the *padas* and safeguarded the manuscripts until her death. In the 17th century, an invasion destroyed everything. Over time, there were many who attempted to erase the memory and music of Mirabai. But the oral tradition of *bhakti* kept her poetry alive and her songs can still be heard to this day in temples and homes throughout India and beyond. Mira's life story and its meaning lie hidden in the devotional *padas* she left. Her story is a sacred myth or legend, like a fairy tale whose symbols must be deciphered by the heart, not by the rational mind.

Where did Mira go? Some say that Raidas came to lead Mira away through a secret underground passage, escaping together into a new existence. Others believe that the devotees kept her safe and hidden within an unknown temple deep in the forests of Vrindavna until old age took her. Some believe that the statue of Krishna came to life and led Mira away through a fissure in the earth. Perhaps she is dancing with the Blue God in the Circle of Divine Love each night.

Some imagine that Mira has become the melody of Krishna's flute, drifting away into the ethereal realms, the place where everything is music and song. Perhaps she entered Asvattha the Cosmic Tree and became one with nature, residing in the realm that is illumined by neither sun, moon, nor fire. Or has Krishna opened His mouth and drawn her into a new life and existence? It may be that in her next life, Mira is given the role of the Old One, the Keeper of the Amulet, guiding other seekers to the Beloved. Or perhaps she walks onstage in this time and place, even now, to sing her songs in concert or temple.

Many believe that the *murti* still exists and has been handed down over the generations to new incarnations of Mirabai, other souls who are the Bearers of Love and Music, continuing the Great *Bhakti* for Krishna. Only the Dark One can answer these riddles. We may ask, if our devotion is great, and perhaps He will tell us the tale. But in the end, it matters not, we must take the legend of Mira-bai on faith alone. She is in the heart of God, in the Realm Beyond Going.

PART III: Through the Blue Door

Recapitulation

1. Drowning in the Ocean of Becoming

O my Beloved, stay before my eyes

Do not forget me,

I am drowning in the Ocean of Becoming,

Remember me soon.

Mira's Lord is the courtly Giridhara,

Do not leave me when once we have met.

(#50 Alston 54-5)

Something warm and wet is nudging me gently, first my arm, then licking my face, then breathing softly in my ear. I am still completely entranced, as though centuries and worlds away. Through the ongoing persistence of this extremely tactile sensation I begin to be aware of myself. Surabhi, the Sacred Cow has come to bring me back and give me rebirth.

Looking down upon the Meditation Hall I hear that the sounds of the chant have peaked and are on the decline in both volume and tempo indicating an ending soon to come. The Call of the Flute has dimmed to a mere whisper, as if the Player has tired and finally run out of inspiration and breath. It seems like only moments ago that the blue child took me by the hand and led me into the temple. And yet, perhaps many lifetimes have passed. Surabhi tells that I must return before the music has ended or I will be unable to re- enter the reality of my time and place.

Part of my soul wants to stay in the eternal Groves of Vrindavana, and I resist the words of Surabhi. But the call of the flute is again becoming more and more insistent; I must return if I want to complete what I have begun in my life, it is not yet finished. Sitting on Her back is the young boy with the crocodile earrings smiling and beckoning me to return to the *lila* or play of life. Although it is entirely my choice, time is of the essence. They both tell me that I must make up my mind in all finality and can never turn back once the resolution is made. I remember the words of instruction from Krishna to Arjuna at the Battle of Kurukshetra: "be true to your destiny," and I choose to fully embrace who I am in the present.

And so I am drawn back again into the Divine Eye, the Womb of Rebirth, making ready to return. I am pushed and pulsated back and forth in waves of energy that are now unstoppable. As the last long breath of the chant dies away, I am thrust back into the Meditation Hall once more in this time and place. When I open my eyes, I am fully present in my body again. The musicians and other devotees have vanished and I am alone in darkness and complete silence. The candles have been extinguished and no one remains to show me out. I discover that the amulet is no longer around my neck. I fear it has been lost back in some ancient time and I will never see it again. And I can no longer hear the Call of the Flute in the utter stillness of this return to the present.

Afterwards, when I return home, I know I have encountered the core meaning of life. I have seen without sight, heard without sound, and felt without touch. I have followed the Secret Path through the Tall Grass and gone to the realm where everything is music and song. But somehow, I cannot quite put my finger on this enigma. It is as though the Veil of Maya has once again descended to obscure the Mysteries in all their esoteric and surreal beauty, protecting them from the outer world and preserving them for the inner.

When I try to make sense of my experience, the images evaporate into nothingness. When I try to describe my vision to others, it comes out as meaningless babble, for no language can ever express the mysteries of the universe. Other times I become mute and no words can pass my paralyzed lips. Friends and acquaintances stare at me in disbelief and dismay as I grasp for ways to explain what has happened to me. I have become unhinged, broken open, turned inside out and upside down. No one recognizes me or knows who I am. No one sees what I have become. I have undergone an initiation that has set me apart from those who have not gone the Way of the Secret Path. Reading Krishna's words in the *Bhagavad Gita*, I am reminded of His final instructions to Arjuna:

> This confidential knowledge may never be explained
>
> To those who are not austere, or devoted,
>
> or engaged in devotional service,
>
> nor to one who is envious of me.
>
> 18.67 (Prabhupada) Lord Krishna, *Bhagavad Gita*

And so I too learn to remain silent and hold this glimpse of the eternal truths close to my heart as a private and personal vision. I understand only that my experience of the secrets of the universe is itself the greatest enigma, which can never be revealed or articulated through human language. Accepting the covenant with the Blue God's injunction to uphold and protect these deepest of mysteries, I have agreed to surrender to that which cannot be spoken and to become a Keeper of Secrets.

2. <u>Coda: The Leaf Doesn't Go Back to the Branch</u>

To be born in a human body is rare,

Don't throw away the reward of your past good deeds.

Life passes in an instant- the leaf doesn't go back to the branch.

The ocean of rebirth sweeps up all beings hard,

Pulls them into its cold-running, fierce, implacable currents.

Giridhara, your name is the raft, the one safe passage over.

Take me quickly.

(Bly/Hirshfield 48) Trans Hirshfield

Trying to recapture my memories, I return to the Chai House. I know this is the same place by its plain, nameless sign. All the surroundings are the same, but I am shocked to find that the shop has changed so dramatically it is almost unrecognizable. It must have been completely remodeled, for the unforgettable Indian style architecture is gone. Instead of an exotic miniature temple, it has been replaced by a modern, boxy building. The large square windows are completely open to the street and I can see plastic bar stools and high tables inside. There is no decor to speak of; the interior has a plain and functional ambience. Unadorned dirty white walls add to the monochromatic blandness of the shop. And the exterior staircase that led to an exquisite balcony is gone.

Still, I am certain it is the right location, so I walk in. The staff is completely unfamiliar to me and when I ask about the re-model they tell me the shop has always been the same. They say that tarot readings have never been offered there. No one remembers any gypsy and their facial expressions show disbelief and confusion at my words. Looking around the room, there is no spiral staircase and it is obvious that the building is all on one floor. And so I leave by the same door I entered, baffled and bewildered. A spark of fear strikes my heart and I wonder if I am awakening and returning to life like Rip Van Winkle, having spent many long years in a fairyland far from this world.

I decide I must return to the Temple of the Peacock. At first I cannot find it and walk around in circles like a lost soul wandering through some unmarked and deserted land. I am completely without a sense of direction, stymied in my efforts. Finally, I stand sobbing and paralyzed in one spot, feeling a bottomless sense of loss and grief in my heart as though I can no longer find my way home. My fantastical journey has shown me that I can never return to what has passed, but perhaps I will move forward to a new place where I belong in the fullness of my being. This hope becomes the guiding light of my heart.

Becoming quiet, I manage to let go of my confusion and calm myself. Slowly memories of a dream-like nature enter my mind. I can remember becoming a powerful Goddess rooted in the Tree of Life and defeating a demon with the healing essence of a tiny teardrop. I remember triumphing over the poison of persecution. I know I have withstood the trials of a desert wasteland, overcoming loss of hope, faith, and identity. I have shared the sacred fruit of the purple plum with an enchanting blue child. I have experienced the time before birth and danced in ecstasy in the mystic Grove of a Blue God. And only then do I know the way to follow the Secret Path through the Tall Grass, for the Call of the Flute is again sounding in my imagination leading me onward.

But when I finally find the temple, it is silent and empty, as if unused for decades. The regal fan of peacock feathers that had adorned the doorway has disappeared. And the birds that guard the entrance are merely decorative, made of dull and colorless wood, inanimate, and crudely carved with none of the sublime artistry I remember seeing in the surreal, lifelike birds. Only one solitary feather lies on the steps, its eye gleaming blankly at me. The temple door is locked and boarded up and the place appears to be abandoned, so neglected that it looks like a long forgotten ruin from an ancient time, ready to cave in and return to the earth.

The entranceway to the walled garden has vanished and the grove of trees filled with purple plums, the color of His skin, no longer exists. Even though I realize full well that no one will come to answer my call, I knock and pound wildly on the front door in frustration and futility until my knuckles are bruised and stinging, as though I could force an answer. Pacing back and forth around the building, I am finally breathless and sobbing with exhaustion. The temple with its grounds is only a one-dimensional empty shell of what it had been. In confusion, I begin to wonder if this is the right place after all or if I had ever been there. Perhaps it was all a dream and I am deluding myself. Perhaps I have gone mad.

I want so badly to see the beautiful blue child again, to hear his laughter, to feel myself melting with joy in his affection, to feel my love wash over him in return, to look deeply into his eyes and see my divinity reflected back to me in all its splendor. I have so many questions to ask about the fantastic experience he has given me. And it is not my curiosity that draws me to him; it is my love, for I would go to the ends of the earth to find him once more. I am bereft with a longing that cannot be fulfilled in the same way for I know I will never see him again in this place. I am inconsolable, sobbing convulsively from the depths of my being, as though my own precious, beloved child is gone and lost to me forever. But strewn around the grounds are some half eaten plums as though a wanderer had rested here and tasted the fruits of paradise. The sight of the plums rekindles a spark of hope in me and a belief in what has been and what may yet come to pass.

When I ask people in the neighborhood about the shrine in the walled garden, they say nothing like that has ever existed in their time. Eventually I meet a very old woman who I could swear is the gypsy reader. But she looks blankly at me without recognition of my face and my questions about the temple baffle her. The core essence of my experience remains with me still, but the details have quickly vanished both in physical reality and in my now uncertain memory. And I have not found the Blue Door without a Key that the Gypsy spoke of. I fear I will never find the way Home.

And so, I return to my old life to find that my experience is like a dream. But when I glance in the mirror, I can still see, through my divinely anointed eye, the glowing outlines of the sacred *tilaka* on my forehead, though no one else in this world seems able to see it. Only then do I remember the words of the Gypsy Reader: "You cannot return the way you came. The leaf doesn't go back to the branch and Life goes always forward." And when I hold the little Krishna to my heart for comfort, I can hear the Call of the Flute.

3. <u>Priestess of Song</u>

It is only when I sing for an audience that I can begin to convey the depth of transformation that has taken place in me. I feel a profound love and dedication towards the music and my listeners in a circle of giving and receiving that has no end. Through my quest, I have been given a boon by the God of Music and Love and have an invaluable gift to offer my audience, greater than any gems that can be found on earth. My musical expression is far deeper than anything I could achieve before. Every concert is a peak experience, a communion with the Divine Muse. And in this I find my solace.

In each city, when I am on stage, I always see the handsome, dark skinned boy with the crocodile earrings in the audience. Every time I am nearly overcome, my heart bursting with excitement and delight that he is here to enjoy my songs. And then it is as though I sing only for him and there is no one else listening, as if he were God. He is my Muse, inspiring my voice to soar, bringing forth gorgeous sounds of unimaginable beauty. Tones and emotions come floating out of the very depths of my being effortlessly, without fear or inhibition.

The anticipation of being with the blue child again after the concert sparks my performance even higher like a burst of adrenaline. But afterwards he is always gone. He seems to disappear into thin air as if by magic. My dressing room remains empty of his bright presence and I know, despite always hoping and waiting with bated breath, that he will not come to greet me. For he belongs to another time and place.

On many evenings, especially when the moon is full, an anonymous basket of dark blue plums awaits me in my dressing room following the recital as a sign of his favor. On top of the plums is a single peacock feather and the arrangement is decorated with garlands of fragile green and purple *tulasi* blossoms to remind me of my Divine Benefactor. And so, I learn once again that I must hold the sacred knowledge inside myself, and with this I am content.

Some time passes and at the autumn full moon in the month of Shravana, the time of the Sacred Circle Dance, I am overjoyed to find the amulet of the dark-skinned flute player resting on the usual basket of plums and blossoms. But then, I do not see the blue boy ever again in the audience. At first I scan the crowded hall with hope and a little fear, missing his beautiful countenance with a bottomless yearning and a gnawing hunger. I break down crying with every thought of him and once again feel the emptiness of his absence as the greatest loss I have ever endured. And yet, my singing remains unaffected and is imbued with even more depth and passion, for somehow the feel of the amulet against my heart chakra gives me courage and faith. And I recall the words of the Gypsy, "All will be well no matter how it may seem."

When I am at the point of drowning in the pain of my heartbreak, The Blue Child comes to me in a numinous vision through the *murti,* calling me with the melody of His flute. His warm dark eyes and his radiant smile reassure me that he has now become one with me and lives and breathes within my very psyche. And I know I will no longer look for him in the mundane realm of my audience or mourn the loss of his physical presence, for his role in my life has been accomplished and completed. The return of the amulet is my gift from him, a reminder that he is with me still in spirit.

I have become enamored of Indian music, particularly the songs of the Poet-Saint Mirabai. I experience her as a living, breathing companion, absolutely real in my perception and I learn many of her heartfelt pieces. There is the odd sensation that I have heard them before but I cannot recall when or where. The music comes to me without effort or study, as though I had sung these stirring melodies throughout my entire career. My method of making the music my own is completely different from the techniques I employed in the past for Mira seems to be guiding me in my interpretation. Now I am singing through instinct and intuition alone, opening myself to

the sensation, emotion, and sound of the music. I hear Mira's melodious, soulful voice singing in my mind and when I begin to repeat
the lines in imitation, the sound is identical. I realize this glorious
and stunning voice is in fact, my own.

For the encore after each performance, I begin offering a *pada* of
Mira. The audience rises up as one in joy and pleasure after each
song, showering me with flowers and calling me back again and
again for yet another. These lovers of the classic art song and aria
have opened their minds and hearts to this exotic and unfamiliar
music, finding that all music is the expression of the universal language of the spirit which is love.

4. <u>The Blue Door</u>

As my memories become more and more vague and fleeting, my recurrent dream has changed. And the nightmare of the desert is gone. Each night in endless variety I am once more dancing in the verdant forests of Vrindavana. I hear the Call of the Flute and my Consort is always the same. He is blue skinned and dusky, crowned with peacock feathers, playing His flute like a magician of sound. And each night I am one with the Eternal Beloved in perpetual joy, as we sing together in harmony a duet of eternal and undying love.

A completely new dream has come to me as well. I have dreamt of a royal wedding, my own wedding. The Bride is addressed as Mira, but when I look upon her face, I see it is my own and I see our shared soul mirrored back to me in all its unique radiance. The *Mandap* or wedding pavilion is the mythical Upside Down Tree *Asvattha* which creates a shaded canopy for the ceremony. It is a wish-fulfilling tree where all of my deepest desires are about to be granted. A golden skinned *pandit* is my priest. Many familiar faces are present as witness, people I recollect as if from a dream or a novel read long ago. They introduce themselves by name: Lalita, Raidas, Bhoj Raj, Sabri, Jiva. I feel so much love for them and gratitude that they are here now to share this sacred moment with me. Others are present who I cannot name but know by their roles in a fantastical legend narrated by the Divine Story Teller: a boatman, a mystic minstrel, a Gypsy reader, a group of sacred dancers, and a loving parental couple. A queenly cow, a peacock, and two white swans are in attendance as well.

I feel the marriage necklace, the *Mangalsutra*, being placed around my neck. It is the amulet with the charm of the Dark-Skinned Flute Player. As I garland my Beloved with *tulasi*, He takes my hand and together we walk the *Saptapadi*, the seven steps of commitment. He is so dark his skin is nearly blue, and he is crowned with peacock feathers and wears a pair of crocodile earrings. In the background accompanied by the flute, I hear the chanting of the sacred wedding mantra: "I am the words and you are the melody, I am the melody and you are the words." Now we are music together, singing from the same Source.

Abruptly the scene changes and my Beloved and I are in another time and place, somewhere eternal beyond the veils of civilization. We are in a lush tropical forest and the greenery is so thick it is impenetrable. It is as though we two are the only beings in the entire universe, safe and protected in this sacred grove. Everything else has disappeared. The call of a flute can be heard, but the Player is hidden and cannot be seen. I have been given the gift of my heart's desire from my Beloved, for in my arms I am holding a beautiful, young boy whose skin is blue velvet, the color of plums. The child is laughing with an ecstatic joy as if at some great cosmic joke as he presses his sweet face to mine with loving affection.

In the center of this magical garden stands a tree, an upside-down tree, roots soaring into the heavens, branches reaching deeply into the earth. It is *Asvattha*, the Cosmic Tree of Life. Standing under the tree within this Garden of Paradise, my beautiful groom begins to metamorphose, both in form and spirit. As He merges with the tree, His body becomes the trunk, strong enough to support the whole world. His arms are branches entwined with leafy greenery, birds of many colors, and precious gems. His legs are roots reaching deeply into the Mother Earth.

To my amazement, He becomes a Blue Door set organically within the Cosmic Tree of Life which holds together the entire universe. This is not a mere slab of inanimate wood, but a living, breathing manifestation of Nature, a doorway into *Nirvana*. As this transformation takes place, the tree bursts into bloom and produces its sacred fruit of deep blue.

I have no key, for there is no key that can unlock the Blue Door. The Divine One reveals the Secret Path that leads through the Tall

Grass and the portal opens for me in welcome. I walk through the Blue Door with the beautiful blue child in my arms and I have come Home, dissolving into the embrace of the Blue God and All That Is.

My daily life has changed along with the dream. The sacred music of the Rasa Lila and the song of Murali permeate all that I do, and each person I encounter is a part of the Beloved of All. My Divine Eye has been anointed, blessed, and opened to an experience of life that is beyond language. Now I know that my Heart's Desire has been with me and in me from the beginning, guiding and inspiring my every breath. Each experience I have been given has led me to this very place where I am meant to be. Reflected in the eyes of the Blue God of Love and Music, the divine splendor I sought was always the fullness of my own soul. And the Call of the Flute draws me ever on to engage in the play of life's adventures. I will leave you with these words of Mirabai from a favorite encore:

The sky ---full of clouds, it's raining.
Joyous I feel, excited,
I have heard Hari will come.
Clouds are everywhere, lightning too,
Raindrops fall,
The gentle breeze gladdens my heart.
Says Mira: My Lord Giridhara,
The moment has come

To sing songs of joy, of love.

(Munshi 74)

ABOUT THE AUTHOR

Born under the sign of the Archer, Ondine Webb De Mer has been a seeker all of her life. Her original degree was a BA in Humanities where she studied Literature, Philosophy, Religion, Art History and Writing. She later attended Music School earning both a Bachelor of Music and a Master of Arts in Piano Performance. She is currently a classical pianist and teacher. Her short stories and articles have appeared in SageWoman, Daughters of Nyx, and Clavier Companion. She has been involved in several different spiritual paths, including Goddess Worship, Siddha Yoga Meditation, the Fellowship of Isis, Interfaith Community Sanctuary, and Dances of Universal Peace. Many of her creative ideas in The Call of the Flute, The Legend of Mirabai originated from actual personal experiences in ritual, chanting, dreams, tarot, psychedelic drugs, and piano performance.

Made in the USA
Columbia, SC
28 February 2023

13120646R00128